Glencoe Science

Probeware Labs

Using probeware data collection and graphing calculator analysis

Teacher Edition

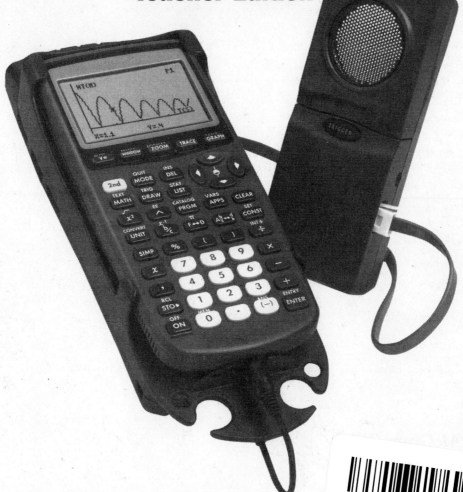

Mc Graw Hill **Glencoe McGraw-Hill**

New York, New York   Columbus, Ohio   Chicago, Illinois   Peoria, Illinois   Woodland Hills, California

Glencoe Science

Credits

The photo of the CBL 2, graphing calculator, and pH probe on the front cover and at the top of the first page of each student lab appears courtesy of Texas Instruments, Inc. Each *Probeware Lab* activity was reviewed by Richard Sorensen, of Vernier Software & Technology.

The terms CBL 2, TI-GRAPH LINK, TI Connect and TI InterActive! are either registered trademarks of, trademarks of, or copyrighted by Texas Instruments, Inc. Vernier LabPro is a registered trademark of and Graphical Analysis is copyrighted by Vernier Software & Technology. Macintosh is a registered trademark of Apple Computer, Inc. Windows is a registered trademark of Microsoft Corporation in the United States and/or other countries.

Glencoe/McGraw-Hill

A Division of The McGraw·Hill Companies

Send all inquiries to:
Glencoe/McGraw-Hill
8787 Orion Place
Columbus, OH 43240

ISBN 0-07-830382-6
Printed in the United States of America
5 6 7 8 9 10   045   10 09 08 07 06 05

Contents

To the Teacher

What are Probeware Labs?

This *Probeware Labs* manual contains 15 probeware laboratory activities that are designed for a middle school life science, Earth science, or physical science curriculum. Each activity helps students explore scientific concepts using a probeware data collection system. These hand-held systems provide a fast and simple way to collect, view, and analyze data in the classroom or during a field investigation. Using various probes and sensors, students can measure temperature, light, voltage, conductivity, motion, pH, and more. Integrating technology in the classroom is made simple with step-by-step instructions for setting up and using the probeware.

What are the components of a probeware system?

- **CBL 2™ or LabPro® data collection unit** collects data from the probes and sends it to the graphing calculator.
- **DataMate** is a software program that is used to collect and plot data. DataMate comes loaded on the CBL 2 or LabPro unit and is transferred to the graphing calculator for use.
- **TI-73 or TI-83 Plus Graphing Calculator** displays and analyzes data. The activities in the manual were written for use with a TI-73 or TI-83 Plus graphing calculator although several other TI graphing calculators are compatible with both data collection units.
- **Probes** collect data. A wide variety of probes are available for the CBL 2 and LabPro systems. A list of the specific probes needed for this book is found on *page 8*.

What does the Teacher Preparation section provide?

- **Purpose** gives a brief description of the objectives of each activity.
- **Time Allotment** provides approximate time requirements for each activity.
- **Advance Preparation** includes instructions on how to prepare activity materials and equipment before the activity begins.
- **Materials** provides additional information about the supplies needed in the activity (i.e. where to obtain the materials or alternate materials).
- **Safety Information** includes safety precautions that you should be aware of and/or make students aware of. This section also includes appropriate disposal precautions.
- **Teaching Tips** provides background knowledge students may need and concepts that should be reviewed before performing the activity.
- **Extension** gives suggestions for extending the learning experience. These include suggestions for other activities that build on the concepts being taught, ideas for modifying and expanding the activity, and ideas for getting students to "extend" their thinking.
- **Pre-Lab Answers** provides correct responses to the student pre-lab questions. These questions are designed to encourage thought and discussion about important concepts needed to successfully complete the activity. Discuss the answers with students to ensure their understanding before they begin the activity.

Safety and Disposal of Lab Materials

Teaching science requires the use of certain supplies and safety equipment to maintain a safe classroom. The activities in *Glencoe Science Probeware Labs* minimize dangers in the laboratory. Even so, there are no guarantees against accidents. For additional help, refer to the booklet *Glencoe Laboratory Management and Safety in the Science Classroom,* which contains safety guidelines and masters to test students' lab and safety skills.

General Guidelines

- Post safety guidelines, fire escape routes, and a list of emergency procedures in the classroom. Make sure students understand these procedures. Remind them at the beginning of *every* lab session.
- Understand and make note of the Safety Symbols used in the activities.
- Have students fill out a safety contract. Students should pledge to follow the rules, to wear safety attire, and to conduct themselves in a responsible manner.
- Know where emergency equipment is stored and how to use it.
- Perform all activities before you allow students to do so.
- Supervise students at all times. Check assembly of all setups.
- Instruct students to follow directions carefully and to not take shortcuts or switch steps.
- Make sure that all students are wearing proper safety attire. Do not permit wearing contact lenses, even with safety glasses; splashing chemicals could infuse under a lens and cause eye damage.

Handling Electronic Equipment

- Instruct students on the safety guidelines provided by the manufacturer of your calculator(s) and probe(s).
- Check wiring for damage before each use. Do not use if frayed.
- Do not use the equipment where it could get wet.
- Do not allow students to eat or drink while using the equipment.
- Unplug the calculator when not in use.

- Caution students to use care when handling the equipment. Calculators and probes should not be shaken or dropped.
- Store the equipment properly when not in use.

Handling Chemicals

- Always wear safety goggles, gloves, and an apron when handling chemicals. Treat all chemicals as potentially dangerous.
- Never ingest chemicals. Use proper techniques to smell solutions.
- Use a fume hood when handling chemicals that are poisonous or corrosive or that give off a vapor.
- Know the location of an eyewash station. Flush the eyewash for five minutes once a week to remove harmful contaminants that may grow in the eyewash. Do not use a squeeze bottle as a substitute for an eyewash.
- Always add acids to water, never the reverse.
- Prepare solutions by adding the solid to a small amount of distilled water and then diluting with water to the volume listed. If you use a hydrate that is different from the one specified in a particular preparation, you will need to adjust the amount of hydrate to obtain the correct concentration.
- Consider purchasing premixed solutions from a scientific supply house to reduce the amount of chemicals on hand.
- Maintain appropriate MSDS (Materials Safety Data Sheets) in the laboratory.

Chemical Storage

- Use wood shelving, rather than metal, that is firmly attached to the wall.
- Equip shelves with a lip to prevent chemicals from being jarred off the shelf.

- Store only those chemicals you intend to use.
- Store chemicals in upright positions no more than three containers deep.
- Store chemicals at or below eye level but not on the floor.
- Make sure all containers are labeled to identify the contents, concentration, date purchased or prepared, safety precautions for handling, expiration date, and manufacturer's name and address.
- Separate chemicals by reaction type. For example, store acids in one place and bases in another. Store oxidants away from easily oxidized materials.
- Store flammables in an approved flammable cabinet.

Chemical Disposal

- Maintain an ongoing chemical inventory. Remove chemicals that are out-of-date, contaminated, or lacking legible labels.
- Consult local and state authorities for disposal methods. Use a reference such as *Prudent Practices in the Laboratory: Handling and Disposal of Chemicals* (National Academy Press, 1995) for general guidelines on handling and disposing of chemicals. Current laws in your area supersede the information in this book.
- Neutralize any substance that has a pH less than 3 or greater than 8 before disposal.

- For substances that can be flushed down a drain, flush with at least 100 times its volume of tap water.
- Consider utilizing a commercial chemical disposal company.

Chemical Spills

- Maintain a clearly identified spill kit in the science lab that contains commercial materials for that purpose. You also can keep a container of dry sand or dry clay available; remember that these will not neutralize an acid or base.
- Contain the spill and neutralize the chemical if necessary.
- Remove the material with equipment made of plastic or polypropylene to prevent reaction with any chemical that remains.
- Place the material in plastic bags or containers and label appropriately.
- Inform the custodial staff of proper disposal of the material.
- For a major spill, such as breaking a liter bottle of hydrochloric acid, take the following actions:
  ➤ Evacuate all students through the exits farthest from the spill.
  ➤ Assist any person splashed with the chemical to the safety shower.
  ➤ Contain the spill wearing proper protective clothing. Do not allow the spill to trap you.
  ➤ Call for help.

DISCLAIMER

Glencoe/McGraw-Hill makes no claims to the completeness of this discussion of laboratory safety and chemical storage. The information presented is not all-inclusive, nor does it address all of the hazards associated with the handling, storage, and disposal of chemicals, or with laboratory practices and management.

Materials

It is assumed that goggles, laboratory aprons, tap water, distilled water, textbooks, paper, calculators, pencils, pens, weighing paper or dishes, and balances are available for all activities. The quantities listed are needed for each individual or group performing the activity.

Probeware Materials	Lab 1	Lab 2	Lab 3	Lab 4	Lab 5	Lab 6	Lab 7	Lab 8	Lab 9	Lab 10	Lab 11	Lab 12	Lab 13	Lab 14	Lab 15
AC adapter, 2			X						X						
Barometer									X						
Chest-belt heart rate monitor		X													
Conductivity probe	X														
Current probe								X							
Light-intensity sensor										X					
Motion detector (sensor)											X				X
pH probe			2			X	X								
Relative humidity sensor									X						
Temperature probe				X	X				X			X	X	X	

Consumable Materials

	Lab 1	Lab 2	Lab 3	Lab 4	Lab 5	Lab 6	Lab 7	Lab 8	Lab 9	Lab 10	Lab 11	Lab 12	Lab 13	Lab 14	Lab 15
Aluminum foil			X												
Bouillon cubes, 3	X														
Cabbage, 1/2 head			X												
Calcium chloride, 5 g													X		
Coffee filter*				X											
Copper magnet wire, enameled								X							
Isopropyl alcohol, 50 mL				X											
Limestone pebbles (pea-sized), 5						X									
Plastic food wrap			X												
Plastic Spoon													X		
Potassium chloride, 5 g													X		
Saline solution, 5% (in dropper or spray bottle)		X													
Salt, non-iodized, 10 g			X												
Sandpaper								X							
Straws, plastic drinking							X								
String					X			X							
Tape, masking								X		X	X			X	
Tube, strong cardboard or plastic								X							

Alternate materials include cotton balls, cotton gauze, or filter paper.

Non-consumable Materials

	Lab 1	Lab 2	Lab 3	Lab 4	Lab 5	Lab 6	Lab 7	Lab 8	Lab 9	Lab 10	Lab 11	Lab 12	Lab 13	Lab 14	Lab 15
100-mL beaker													X		
150-mL beaker						X									
250-mL beaker			2	X											
400-mL beaker	X		X			X							X	X	

Non-consumable Materials, cont.	Lab 1	Lab 2	Lab 3	Lab 4	Lab 5	Lab 6	Lab 7	Lab 8	Lab 9	Lab 10	Lab 11	Lab 12	Lab 13	Lab 14	Lab 15
600-mL beaker							X								
Bar magnet, strong								X							
Beaufort wind scale									X						
Board															X
Chair								X							
Cloud chart									X						
Drawing compass					X										
Electric fan				X											
Hot mitt or thermal glove												2		X	
Hot plate														X	
Jar, glass, 1-L						X									
Jar, plastic with lid												X			
Lamp, with 60-watt incadescent bulb										X					
Meterstick or measuring tape					X					X	X				
Protractor					X										
Ring stand with test-tube clamp, 2			X												
Rubber band, small				X											
Ruler, metric	X							X							
Sand, 250 mL												X			
Spoon, plastic													X		
Stirring rod, glass			X										X		
Table								X							
Test strips of materials (see lab 14 for details)														X	
Timer or stopwatch		X					X					X			
Tongs			X												
Toy car or lab cart															X
Transparencies, 10					X										
Transparency markers, colored					X										
Trowel					X										
Wash bottle			X				X								
Wooden dowels or craft sticks, 8					X										

Suppliers

Sources of Probeware

Vernier Software & Technology
13979 SW Millikan Way
Beaverton, OR 97005-2886
(503) 277-2299
info@vernier.com
www.vernier.com

Texas Instruments
Customer Support
P.O. Box 650311, MS 3962
Dallas, TX 75265
(800) 842-2737
ti-cares@ti.com
www.ti.com

PASCO Scientific
10101 Foothills Blvd.
P.O. Box 619011
Roseville, CA 95747-9011
(800) 772-8700
sales@pasco.com
www.pasco.com

Equipment Suppliers

Science Kit and Boreal Laboratories
777 East Park Drive
P.O. Box 5003
Tonawanda, NY 14151-5003
(800) 828-7777
sk@sciencekit.com
www.sciencekit.com

Flinn Scientific, Inc.
770 N. Raddant Rd.
P.O. Box 219
Batavia, IL 60510
(800) 452-1261
flinn@flinnsci.com
www.flinnsci.com

Frey Scientific
100 Paragon Parkway
P.O. Box 8105
Mansfield, OH 44903
(800) 225-3739
customercare@freyscientific.com
www.freyscientific.com

Fisher Science Education
4500 Turnberry
Hanover Park, IL 60133
(800) 955-1177
info@fisheredu.com
www.fisheredu.com

Carolina Biological Supply Co.
2700 York Road
Burlington, NC 27215-3398
(800) 334-5551
www.carolina.com

Scientific Company
60 Pearce Ave.
Tonawanda, NY 14150-6711
(800) 728-6999
scientifics@edsci.com
www.scientificsonline.com

Nasco Science
901 Janesville Ave.
P.O. Box 901
Fort Atkinson, WI 53538-0901
(800) 558-9595
www.enasco.com

Nebraska Scientific
3823 Leavenworth St.
Omaha, NE 68105-1180
(800) 228-7117
staff@nebraskascientific.com
www.nebraskascientific.com

Sargent-Welch/VWR Scientific Products
911 Commerce Court
P.O. Box 5229
Buffalo Grove, IL 60089-5229
(800) 727-4368
sarwel@sargentwelch.com
www.SargentWelch.com

Ward's Natural Science
5100 W. Henrietta Road
P.O. Box 92912
Rochester, NY 14692-9012
(800) 962-2660
customerservice@wardsci.com
www.wardsci.com

To the Student

The activities in this book are designed to help you study science using probeware technology. A probeware lab is different from other labs because it uses a probe or sensor to collect data, a data collection unit to interpret and store the data, and a graphing calculator or computer to analyze the data. These components are connected with a software program called DataMate that makes them work together in an easy-to-use, handheld, system. These labs are designed specifically for the TI-73 or TI-83 Plus graphing calculators and a CBL 2™ (produced by Texas Instruments, Inc.) or LabPro® (produced by Vernier Software & Technology) data collection unit.

The activities in this book will help you improve your ability to recognize and use equipment properly and to analyze data. To help you get started, the next few pages will provide you with:

- information about **getting started with probeware**
- a list of **laboratory and safety guidelines**
- a reference page of **safety symbols**

Each lab activity in this manual includes the following sections:

- **Introduction** provides a background discussion about the concepts you will study in the activity.
- **What You'll Investigate** contains questions that will be answered by completing the activity.
- **Goals** are statements of what you should accomplish during the activity.
- **Materials** lists the supplies and equipment you will need for the activity.
- **Safety Precautions** warn you of potential hazards in the laboratory. Before beginning any activity, refer to the list of safety symbols in page *viii* to see what each symbol means and take the necessary precautions.
- **Pre-Lab Questions** review your knowledge of important concepts needed to complete the activity successfully. Make sure that you discuss and understand the answers to these questions before you begin each investigation.
- **Procedure** includes numbered steps that tell you how to carry out the activity.
- **Cleanup and Disposal** provides instructions for cleaning equipment and your lab area. Instructions also are given for proper disposal of any wastes.
- **Conclude and Apply** includes a data table or other means for writing your laboratory data. Remember to always record data and observations in an organized way as you do the activity. This section also may show you how to perform the calculations necessary for you to analyze your data and reach conclusions. It provides questions to aid you in interpreting data and observations to help you reach an experimental result.

Getting Started with Probeware

The following instructions will guide you through the setup process for the data collection unit and the graphing calculator. The activities are compatible with either the CBL 2 or the LabPro unit. Each activity was written for use with TI-73 or TI-83 Plus graphing calculators. These activities can be adapted for use with other graphing calculators or other data collection units, if desired.

Connecting a Graphing Calculator to the CBL 2 or LabPro Unit

1. Insert batteries into the CBL 2 or LabPro unit and graphing calculator.

2. The cradle is an optional accessory that conveniently connects the two units. Slide the back of the cradle onto the front of the CBL 2 or LabPro unit until it clicks into place.

3. Insert the upper end of the calculator into the cradle and press down on the lower end until it locks into place.

4. Connect the CBL 2 or LabPro unit to the graphing calculator using the unit-to-unit link cable. Plug the cable into the I/O port at the end of the CBL 2 or LabPro unit and the other end into the I/O port at the end of the calculator. Make sure that the unit-to-unit link cable is securely in place.

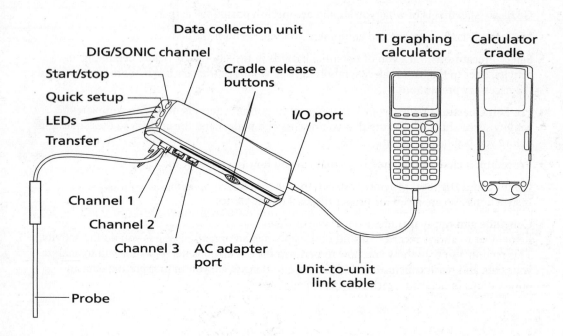

v

Resetting the Calculator Memory

It is recommended that the memory of the calculator be cleared before the DataMate data collection program is transferred.

1. Press ⌷2nd⌷ [MEM].

2. Select **Reset.**

3. Select **ALL RAM…**

4. Select **Reset.** The calculator screen
   will display **RAM cleared.**

Transferring DataMate to the Calculator

The DataMate program is stored on the CBL 2 or LabPro unit and is transferred to the graphing calculator for use. Once DataMate is transferred to the graphing calculator, it will remain there until the calculator memory is reset using the instructions above.

1. For the TI-73, press ⌷APPS⌷. Select **Link…**

   For the TI-83 Plus, press ⌷2nd⌷ [LINK].

2. Use the right arrow to highlight **RECEIVE.** Press ⌷ENTER⌷.

3. The screen will display **Waiting...** Press the large **TRANSFER** key found on the upper left-hand side of the CBL 2 or LabPro unit. When the transfer is complete, the screen will display the transferred programs followed by the word **Done.**

4. Press ⌷2nd⌷ [QUIT].

Starting DataMate

When you are ready to collect data, use the following instructions to start DataMate.

For the TI-73:

1. Press ⌷PRGM⌷.

2. Select **DataMate.**

3. Press ⌷ENTER⌷.

For the TI-83 Plus:

1. Press ⌷APPS⌷.

2. Select **DataMate.**

Setting up Probes Manually

The CBL 2 and LabPro unit should recognize the probe attached automatically. If this does not happen, follow these instructions.

1. Select **SETUP** from the DataMate main screen.

2. Press ⌷ENTER⌷ to select channel 1, or select the channel where the probe is inserted.

3. Select the correct sensor number from the SELECT SENSOR menu.

4. If requested, select the type of probe used.

5. Select **OK** to return to the DataMate main screen.

vi

Laboratory and Safety Guidelines

Emergencies

- Inform the teacher immediately of *any* mishap—fire, injury, glassware breakage, chemical spills, and so forth.
- Know the location of the fire extinguisher, safety shower, eyewash, fire blanket, and first-aid kit. Know how to use this equipment.
- If chemicals come into contact with your eyes or skin, flush with large quantities of water and notify your teacher immediately.

Preventing Accidents

- Do NOT wear clothing that is loose enough to catch on anything. Do NOT wear sandals or open-toed shoes. Remove loose jewelry—chains or blacelets—while doing lab work.
- Wear protective safety gloves, goggles, and aprons as instructed.
- Always wear safety goggles (not glasses) in the laboratory.
- Wear goggles throughout the entire activity, cleanup, and handwashing.
- Keep your hands away from your face while working in the laboratory.
- Remove synthetic fingernails before working in the lab (these are highly flammable).
- Do NOT use hair spray, mousse, or other flammable hair products just before or during laboratory work where an open flame is used (they can ignite easily).
- Tie back long hair and loose clothing to keep them away from flames and equipment.
- Eating, drinking, chewing gum, applying makeup, and smoking are prohibited in the laboratory.
- Do NOT inhale vapors or taste, touch, or smell any chemical or substance unless instructed to do so by your teacher.

Working in the Laboratory

- Study all instructions before you begin a laboratory or field activity. Ask questions if you do not understand any part of the activity.
- Work ONLY on activities assigned by your teacher. NEVER work alone in the laboratory.
- Do NOT substitute other chemicals/substances for those listed in your activity.
- Do NOT begin any activity until directed to do so by your teacher.
- Do NOT handle any equipment without specific permission.
- Remain in your own work area unless given permission by your teacher to leave it.
- Do NOT point heated containers—test tubes, flasks, and so forth—at yourself or anyone else.
- Do NOT take any materials or chemicals out of the classroom.
- Stay out of storage areas unless you are instructed to be there and are supervised by your teacher.

Laboratory Cleanup

- Keep work, lab, and balance areas clean, limiting the amount of easily ignitable materials.
- Turn off all burners, water faucets, probeware, and calculators before leaving the lab.
- Carefully dispose of waste materials as instructed by your teacher.
- With your goggles on, wash your hands thoroughly with soap and warm water after each activity.

Safety Symbols

SAFETY SYMBOLS	HAZARD	EXAMPLES	PRECAUTION	REMEDY
DISPOSAL	Special disposal procedures need to be followed.	certain chemicals, living organisms	Do not dispose of these materials in the sink or trash can.	Dispose of wastes as directed by your teacher.
BIOLOGICAL	Organisms or other biological materials that might be harmful to humans	bacteria, fungi, blood, unpreserved tissues, plant materials	Avoid skin contact with these materials. Wear mask or gloves.	Notify your teacher if you suspect contact with material. Wash hands thoroughly.
EXTREME TEMPERATURE	Objects that can burn skin by being too cold or too hot	boiling liquids, hot plates, dry ice, liquid nitrogen	Use proper protection when handling.	Go to your teacher for first aid.
SHARP OBJECT	Use of tools or glassware that can easily puncture or slice skin	razor blades, pins, scalpels, pointed tools, dissecting probes, broken glass	Practice common-sense behavior and follow guidelines for use of the tool.	Go to your teacher for first aid.
FUME	Possible danger to respiratory tract from fumes	ammonia, acetone, nail polish remover, heated sulfur, moth balls	Make sure there is good ventilation. Never smell fumes directly. Wear a mask.	Leave foul area and notify your teacher immediately.
ELECTRICAL	Possible danger from electrical shock or burn	improper grounding, liquid spills, short circuits, exposed wires	Double-check setup with teacher. Check condition of wires and apparatus.	Do not attempt to fix electrical problems. Notify your teacher immediately.
IRRITANT	Substances that can irritate the skin or mucous membranes of the respiratory tract	pollen, moth balls, steel wool, fiberglass, potassium permanganate	Wear dust mask and gloves. Practice extra care when handling these materials.	Go to your teacher for first aid.
CHEMICAL	Chemicals that can react with and destroy tissue and other materials	bleaches such as hydrogen peroxide; acids such as sulfuric acid, hydrochloric acid; bases such as ammonia, sodium hydroxide	Wear goggles, gloves, and an apron.	Immediately flush the affected area with water and notify your teacher.
TOXIC	Substance may be poisonous if touched, inhaled, or swallowed	mercury, many metal compounds, iodine, poinsettia plant parts	Follow your teacher's instructions.	Always wash hands thoroughly after use. Go to your teacher for first aid.
OPEN FLAME	Open flame may ignite flammable chemicals, loose clothing, or hair	alcohol, kerosene, potassium permanganate, hair, clothing	Tie back hair. Avoid wearing loose clothing. Avoid open flames when using flammable chemicals. Be aware of locations of fire safety equipment.	Notify your teacher immediately. Use fire safety equipment if applicable.

Eye Safety Proper eye protection should be worn at all times by anyone performing or observing science activities.

Clothing Protection This symbol appears when substances could stain or burn clothing.

Animal Safety This symbol appears when safety of animals and students must be ensured.

Radioactivity This symbol appears when radioactive materials are used.

Size Limits of Cells

Purpose

Students will investigate how the surface area of a cell limits the cell's size. Bouillon cubes are used to model cells. When a bouillon cube is cut into pieces, the total volume is unchanged, but the total surface area increases. This results in the faster release of sodium ions and chloride ions into the water. Students will use the CBL 2 unit, a conductivity probe, and a graphing calculator to observe how the conductivity of the solution rises faster with increased surface area. Analysis questions help students to recognize the relationship between the surface area of a cell or cells and the rate at which the cells take in and release substances.

Time Requirements

one 45-minute class period for data collection
one 45-minute class period for analysis

Advance Preparation

The DataMate program should be installed on the graphing calculators.

Safety Information

Remind students that they should never eat or drink any materials used in an experiment.

Teaching Tips

- Review with students how to calculate volume ($V = l \times w \times h$). Demonstrate for students how the volume of a large cube is equal to the volume of that same cube broken into smaller pieces.

- Review with students how to calculate the surface area of a rectangular solid.
- Demonstrate for students how the surface area of a large cube is *less* than the surface area of that same cube broken into smaller pieces. Remind students that you are comparing the surface area of the large cube to the *combined* surface areas of the smaller pieces.
- Review with students how the surface area affects the rate of dissolving of a solid. The sodium and chloride ions that are on the surface of a bouillon cube are exposed to water and will dissolve. The greater the surface area, the faster the rate of dissolving. Therefore, cutting a large cube into several smaller cubes will increase the rate of dissolving.
- Review with students what conductivity is. Review how the conductivity of a solution depends on the amount of ions in the solution. The presence of ions in a solution can be measured by measuring the conductivity of the solution.
- Review with students how substances move into and out of a cell. In this lab, a large bouillon cube is a model for a large cell. The broken pieces of a bouillon cube are a model for several smaller cells. Remind students that you are comparing equal volumes but different surface areas.
- In this lab, the exchange of ions between a bouillon cube and the surrounding water is a model for the movement of substances into and out of a cell. The amount of substances that move through the membranes of several smaller cells is greater than the amount that moves through the membrane of one large cell.

Teacher Preparation (continued)

Extensions

- After performing the experiment, some students may question why some cells can be large. Have them investigate why this is true. For example, the ostrich egg is composed of mostly inactive material and contains a food supply. It doesn't require a high surface-to-volume ratio to obtain the nutrients it needs. Nerve cells can be large because they are long and narrow, giving them a greater surface area.
- Have students research how cells move materials across the cell membrane from an area of high concentration to an area of lower concentration, which is against the natural flow.
- Students can investigate the various types of active transport that different types of cells use to move materials across the cell membrane.
- Students can investigate how some cell membranes are semipermeable and selectively permeable.

Approximate dimensions of the whole cube, half cube, and quarter cube are shown below.

Pre-Lab Answers

1. Electrical conductivity is the ability of a substance to transmit an electric charge.

2. The conductivity would increase, because there are more particles to conduct the charge.

3. The rate will increase because there is more area for the transfer to take place.

A sample graph of conductivity is shown below.

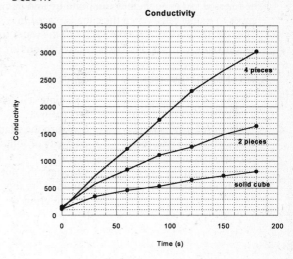

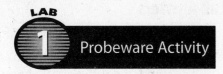

Probeware Activity

Size Limits of Cells

When you look at a leaf under a microscope, you notice that is made of small, rectangular structures—cells. A plant cell constantly absorbs substances it needs to live and gives off waste products through its cell membrane and cell wall. The rate at which these processes can happen depends on the surface area of a cell or group of cells. If the surface area of a cell is too small for a given cell volume, the cell cannot take in substances fast enough to survive. Also, if wastes cannot be released fast enough, they can build up and damage the cell. In this lab, you will use bouillon cubes to model cells. When the cube is placed in water, the cube begins to dissolve into ions. The released ions increase the ability of the water to conduct electricity. By measuring the water's conductivity, you will observe how fast the ions are being released.

What You'll Investigate

- How does the surface area of cells affect the rate at which substances can be absorbed and released?
- How does the surface area of cells limit the size of an individual cell?

Goals

Calculate cell volumes and surface areas.
Measure the change in conductivity of solutions over time.
Compare the rate at which conductivity increases for various solutions.

Materials

CBL 2 or LabPro unit
TI graphing calculator
link cable
DataMate program
conductivity probe
400-mL beaker
distilled water
3 bouillon cubes (1 whole, 1 cut into two equal pieces, 1 cut into four equal pieces)
metric ruler

Safety Precautions

- **CAUTION:** Never eat or drink any substances used in an experiment.
- The conductivity probe is fragile. Handle it carefully.

Pre-Lab

1. Define electrical conductivity.

2. Predict how the number of conducting particles in a solution affects the conductivity of the solution.

3. If a solid is broken into many smaller pieces, how will the rate at which the number of particles entering or leaving the solid be affected?

Lab 1   **1**

Probeware Activity 1 (continued)

Procedure

Part A: Preparing the CBL System

1. Set up the calculator and CBL 2 unit, as shown in **Figure 1**. Set the range on the conductivity probe to 0–20,000 μS. Plug the conductivity probe into channel 1 of the CBL 2 unit.

2. Turn on the calculator and start DataMate. Press CLEAR to reset the program. The conductivity sensor should automatically be recognized. If not, turn to page *vi* for instructions on how to set up the probe manually.

Figure 1

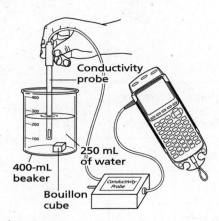

Part B: Collecting Data

1. Using a metric ruler, measure the length, width, and height of a bouillon cube in centimeters. Write these dimensions in **Data Table 1** and in **Figure 2**.

2. Pour 250 mL of distilled water into a 400-mL beaker. Gently place the cube into the water.

3. Lower the conductivity probe into the water until it is about 1 cm above the cube. Select **START** to begin the three-minute measurement.

4. Gently swirl the conductivity probe in the water. The open end of the probe should be submerged but not hitting the bouillon cube.

5. After the measurement has ended, remove the probe and rinse it in distilled water. Set it aside carefully.

6. Press ENTER to go to the main screen. Select **TOOLS.** Then select **STORE LATEST RUN.**

7. Repeat steps 2–6 with two cube halves.

8. Repeat steps 2–6 with four cube quarters. The time measurements will be stored in List 1 (L1). The conductivity measurements will be stored in L4 (whole cube), L3 (two cube halves), and L2 (four cube quarters).

Part C: Graphing Data

1. From the main menu, select **GRAPH.** A graph will appear on the screen.

2. Press ENTER. Select **MORE.** A menu will appear that will allow you to select the desired graph.

3. Select **L2, L3, AND L4 vs L1.** A single graph with three curves will appear.

4. Sketch and label this graph in the space provided on the following page. Be sure to label the curves *whole cube, halved cube,* or *quartered cube.*

5. When you are finished with the graph, press ENTER. Select **QUIT.** Follow the directions on the calculator screen.

Cleanup and Disposal

1. Turn off the graphing calculator and disconnect the conductivity probe and CBL 2.

2. The conductivity probe is fragile. Carefully rinse and dry the probe.

3. Clean and return all equipment as directed by your teacher.

Probeware Activity 1 (continued)

Sketch of Conductivity Graph

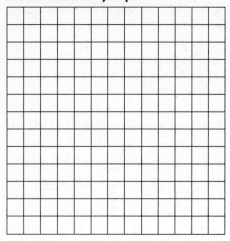

Figure 2

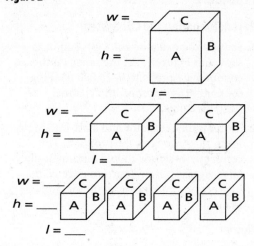

Data Table 1: Calculating Total Volume

	Length (cm)	Width (cm)	Height (cm)	Volume of One Piece	Number of Pieces	Total Volume of All Pieces
Whole cube	1.3	1.3	1.3	2.2	1	2.2
Halved cube	1.3	1.3	0.65	1.1	2	2.2
Quartered cube	0.65	1.3	0.65	0.55	4	2.2

Data Table 2: Calculating Total Surface Area

	Area of Side A (cm²)	Area of Side B (cm²)	Area of Side C (cm²)	Total Surface Area of One Piece	Number of Pieces	Total Area of All Pieces
Whole cube	1.7	1.7	1.7	10.2	1	10.2
Halved cube	0.85	0.85	1.7	6.8	2	13.6
Quartered cube	0.42	0.85	0.85	4.24	4	17

Probeware Activity 1 (continued)

Part D: Analyzing Data

1. Calculate the volume of the whole bouillon cube ($V = l \times w \times h$).

2. Using **Figure 2** as a guide, calculate the length, width, and height of a half cube and a quarter cube. Write these in the spaces provided in **Figure 2** and in **Data Table 1.** Check these with your teacher before proceeding.

3. Calculate the volume of each type of piece—a whole cube, a half cube, and a quarter cube. Enter these values in **Data Table 1.**

4. In **Data Table 1,** write the total number of pieces that are obtained when a whole cube is halved and when a whole cube is quartered.

5. Calculate the total volume of a whole cube, two cube halves, and four cube quarters and write these values in **Data Table 1.**

6. Using **Figure 2** as a guide, calculate the surface areas ($SA = l \times w$) of sides A, B, and C of a whole cube, a half cube, and a quarter cube. Write these in **Data Table 2.** Check these with your teacher before proceeding.

7. Calculate the total surface area of a whole cube, a half cube, and a quarter cube using the formula: Total SA = 2A + 2B + 2C. Why is the surface area of each side multiplied by two?

8. In **Data Table 1,** write the total number of pieces that are obtained when a whole cube is halved and when a whole cube is quartered.

9. Calculate the total surface area of a whole cube, two cube halves, and four cube quarters and write these values in **Data Table 1.**

Conclude and Apply

1. Compare the total volumes of the whole cube, the halved cube, and the quartered cube. Explain your observation. Compare the total surface areas of whole cube, the halved cube, and the quartered cube. What do you observe?

   The volumes of all three are equal because cutting a cube doesn't change the total volume.

   The surface area increased each time the cube was cut.

2. What do you observe about the conductivity of all three bouillon-cube solutions as time progressed? Explain your observations.

   As time progressed, the conductivity of all three solutions increased. As the cubes dissolved, more

   ions were released into the solution, increasing the conductivity.

3. Explain the differences between the three conductivity curves. Which curve shows the fastest rate of dissolving? Explain your observations.

   The cube cut into four pieces dissolved the fastest because it had more surface area exposed

   to the water.

4. Which will allow a greater volume of substances to move into and out of a cell in a given amount of time—one large cell or an equal volume of several smaller cells? Explain.

   Because several smaller cells have a greater surface area than one large cell, a greater volume

   of substances will move into and out of several smaller cells in a given time.

LAB 2 Teacher Preparation

Exercise and Heart Rate

Purpose

Students will investigate one component of the human circulatory system as they study the concepts of constancy, change, and equilibrium. Students will use the graphing calculator, the CBL 2 unit, and a chest-belt heart rate monitor. By collecting heart rate data while at rest, while exercising, and cooling down, students can observe the effect of these changes on the human heart. Students will use graphs and one-variable statistics to compare the class data.

Time Requirements

two 45-minute class periods

Advance Preparation

- The belt electrodes need to be moistened with an electrolyte. Prepare a 5% saline solution by dissolving 5 g of salt per 100 mL of water. Put the solution into the dropper bottles. Contact lens saline solution also can be used.
- Demonstrate the use of the chest belt prior to the lab. It requires skin contact and placement under one's clothing. Students may wish to wear a baggy T-shirt for the lab. Provide a privacy screen for students to use when they put on the monitor. Allow students to pair with a friend.
- Arrange to have steps or stools for the exercise portion of the lab.
- Demonstrate how to do the exercise portion of the lab so all students use the same method and pace.
- Provide an alternative exercise for students who are unable to do the stepping protocol.

Safety Information

- Physical activity can aggravate certain health conditions. Ask students to inform you if they have such a condition.

- Do not force any student to do physical activity. To avoid singling out students who are uncomfortable exercising in front of their peers, allow one student in each group to record data.
- Consult your principal as to whether a permission slip is necessary before proceeding.
- Have some alcohol wipes available or follow your school's policy for cleaning the belt. Show students how to clean the belt between each user.

Teaching Tips

- Help students recall prior knowledge by having them relate experiences they have had with heart rate monitors in physical education class, as members of sports teams, or in athletic clubs.
- Review the circulatory and respiratory systems and how they interact. Ask students to share what they know about these systems.
- Review with students how the heart-rate monitor works. A human being is like a battery powered electrical device—it works electrochemically. When the heart beats, it emits an electric signal which can be picked up by the belt. The belt transmits the signal to the receiver. The receiver is the small box that plugs into the CBL 2. Then, like a radio, the signal is converted into the numbers and points you see on the graphing calculator.
- Review statistical concepts such as mean, median, and mode.
- This activity could be team taught with a physical education teacher. The data can be collected during physical education class and displayed and analyzed in science class.
- Discuss with students what maximum exercise heart rate and exercise intensity level are. Explain how these are used to determine the intensity at which a person is exercising.

Teacher Preparation (continued)

Extensions

1. Investigate other variables. Type of exercise, exercise location (air-conditioned indoor room verses outdoors), sitting verses standing rest, and body posture/position are all possible investigations.

2. Team with the home economics, health, and PE teachers to have a "healthy heart day." Focus lessons on cardiovascular health including nutrition and aerobic training.

3. Organize a community service event such as Hoops for Heart, a basketball skills and games fundraiser for the American Heart Association. The AHA also has brochures, videos, and other educational resources.

4. Research types of heart rate monitors.

5. Have girls check out *Girl Power!*, a national public education campaign sponsored by the U.S. Department of Health and Human Services that seeks to reinforce and sustain positive attitudes and self-esteem among girls ages 9–14 by targeting health messages to the unique needs, interests, and challenges of girls.

Pre-Lab Answers

1. Answers will vary. A student's resting heart rate is usually between 80 and 100 beats per minute.

2. Refer to the explanation provided in the Teaching Tips.

3. By visually displaying the data on a graph and by determining statistical values such as mean, median, and mode.

A sample heart rate graph is shown below. The spike in the graph is due to a sudden increase in stepping speed. For this reason, students should maintain a constant stepping speed.

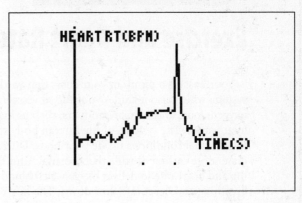

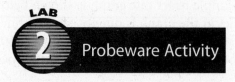

Probeware Activity

Exercise and Heart Rate

Your heart is a pump in your chest that works all day, every day. It is part of your cardiovascular system, which also includes your blood vessels and blood. The cardiovascular system transports oxygen, food, and cellular products, such as insulin, to cells in your body. It also carries away cellular wastes. The systems of the human body strive for equilibrium. They work together to maintain normal conditions inside your body. During exercise, your muscles use more oxygen and generate more carbon dioxide than normal. Your brain senses this change and increases your breathing and heart rate to deliver oxygen-rich blood more quickly. When you finish exercising, your breathing and heart rate slow down. The heart rate of a physically fit person increases less during exercise and returns to normal more quickly than that of a less fit person.

One way you can investigate your heart's health is to count the number of times your heart beats in one minute. You may have done this before by lightly resting your fingers on your neck or wrist. It is called "taking your pulse." In this lab, you will use an electronic heart rate monitor. You will investigate the heart rates of you and your classmates while at rest and while exercising. You will use a graphing calculator to display and analyze your data.

What You'll Investigate

- What is your resting heart rate?
- What effect does exercise have on your heart rate?
- How long does it take your heart rate to return to normal after exercise?

Goals

Collect heart rate data.
Observe and measure the effect of exercise on heart rate.
Compare and analyze heart rate data using statistics.

Materials

CBL 2 unit
TI graphing calculator
link cable
DataMate program
chest-belt heart rate monitor
saline solution in a dropper
   or spray bottle
stopwatch

Safety Precautions

- Inform your teacher if you have any health condition that might be aggravated by physical exercise.
- If during the exercise portion of this activity you feel dizzy, faint, or unwell, stop to rest and tell your teacher.

Pre-Lab

1. Predict your own heart rate in beats per minute.
2. Examine the heart rate monitor. How do you think it works?
3. How can you compare the data for the whole class?

Probeware Activity 2 (continued)

Procedure

Part A: Preparing the CBL System

1. Set up the calculator and CBL 2 unit, as shown in **Figure 1.** Plug the heart rate receiver into channel 1 of the CBL 2 unit.

Figure 1

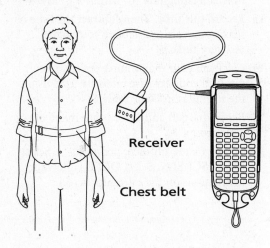

Receiver

Chest belt

2. Turn on the calculator and start DataMate. Press CLEAR to reset the program. The heart rate monitor should be recognized automatically. If not, turn to page *vi* for instructions on how to set up the probe manually.

3. Select **SETUP** on the DataMate main screen to set up the time interval between data points and the length of time the data will be collected.

4. Press the up arrow once until the cursor is beside the **MODE** line. Press ENTER.

5. Select **TIME GRAPH.** Select **CHANGE TIME SETTINGS.** The screen will display "Enter time between samples in seconds."

6. Press 5 ENTER. The screen will display "Enter number of samples."

7. Press 1 0 0. Select **OK.** Select **OK** again. The calculator and CBL 2 unit are ready to obtain a heart rate reading every 5 seconds for 500 seconds.

Part B: Collecting Data

1. Put on a chest belt, selecting an elastic belt that fits snugly around your chest under your shirt. Secure one end of the elastic strap to the plastic transmitter.

2. Moisten the transmitter electrodes with saline solution.

3. Adjust and secure the belt in place over the base of your rib cage with the logo centered in the front.

4. Sit down. Have a partner hold the CBL 2 with the attached receiver module of the monitor. The receiver must remain within 80 cm of the transmitter belt.

5. Sit quietly for one minute to establish normal pulse and to ensure that the monitor is working.

6. Your partner should select **START** on the graphing calculator and start the stopwatch at the same time.

7. Sit quietly for 150 seconds.

8. When 150 seconds have elapsed, begin to exercise by stepping up onto the step and down again. Always place one foot and then the other completely on the surface of the step and floor. Exercise at a relaxed, even pace for 150 seconds.

9. When 150 seconds of exercise have elapsed, sit and rest quietly for 200 seconds. The graphing calculator will display a graph when the time is complete.

10. Sketch this graph in your **Science Journal.** Include a title, labels, and units for the *x*- and *y*-axis.

Copyright © Glencoe/McGraw-Hill, a division of the McGraw-Hill Companies, Inc.

Probeware Activity 2 (continued)

Part C: Examining the Data

1. Return to the main screen by pressing ENTER.
2. Select **ANALYZE.**
3. Select **STATISTICS.**
4. Press ENTER to select the beginning of the initial resting phase. Use the right arrow key to select the end of the resting phase at about 150 seconds and press ENTER.
5. Record the MEAN resting heart rate, rounding to the nearest whole beat per minute (BPM).
6. Press ENTER. Select **STATISTICS.**
7. Use the arrow keys to select the beginning and end of the exercise period. Press ENTER.
8. Record the MEAN exercise heart rate, rounding to the nearest whole beat per minute.
9. Press ENTER. Then select **RETURN TO THE MAIN SCREEN.** Select **GRAPH.**

10. Use the right arrow to move to the highest point on the graph.
11. Record the y-value (maximum heart rate) and x-value (time) that the maximum occurred.
12. Use the right arrow key to find the time when your heart beat had returned to its normal resting rate (to within 3 BPM).
13. Record this time. Then subtract the time of maximum rate to calculate your actual recovery time.
14. Calculate your maximum exercise heart rate and your exercise intensity level using the formulas in **Data Table 1.**
15. Repeat parts **B** and **C** for other members of your group.
16. When you are finished, press ENTER. Select **MAIN SCREEN.** Select **QUIT.** Follow the instructions on the calculator screen.

Data Table 1: Heart Rate Monitor Experiment

Student:	A	B	C
Mean resting heart rate (mean BPM over the first 150 seconds)	90 BPM		
Mean exercise heart rate (mean BPM over the second 150 seconds)	134 BPM		
Maximum heart rate (BPM)	142 BPM		
Time at maximum heart rate (seconds)	300 s		
Time of return to mean resting heart rate (seconds)	360 s		
Recovery time (seconds)	60 s		
Maximum exercise heart rate (MEHR = 220 − your age)	175 BPM		
Exercise intensity level (%) = (exercise heart rate/MEHR) × 100	77%		

Cleanup and Disposal

1. Turn off the calculator. Unplug the receiver module from the CBL 2.
2. Separate the elastic strap and the transmitter belt.
3. Clean the transmitter belt as instructed by your teacher.
4. Return the heart rate monitor and CBL 2 system as directed by your teacher.

Probeware Activity 2 (continued)

Conclude and Apply

1. Describe the effect that exercise had on your heart rate.

Answers should reflect that exercise increased heart rate, perhaps including the amount or

percentage of increase.

2. Share data with your classmates for resting heart rate, exercise heart rate, and recovery time. Design a data table to organize this information.
Check students' tables.

3. With your lab partners, divide the responsibility for constructing a histogram of the class data for each variable: resting heart rate, exercise heart rate, and recovery time. Your teacher may give you directions for using the graphing calculator to do this.
Instructions for creating a histogram are given in appendices A and B.

4. Determine the minimum, median, maximum, mean, and mode for each data set from the class. Record these in **Data Table 2**. Your teacher may give you directions for doing this with the graphing calculator.
Instructions for determining statistics are given in appendices C and D.

Data Table 2: Class Statistics

	Resting Heart Rate (BPM)	Exercise Heart Rate (BPM)	Recovery Time (seconds)
Minimum			
Median			
Maximum			
Mean			
Mode			

5. You can visually display information such as you have in **Data Table 2** using a box plot. Your teacher may give you directions for making a box plot using your graphing calculator. Compare and contrast this method of displaying data with the "data table method" used in Question 4.
Instructions for creating a box plot are given in appendices C and D.

6. What can you conclude about heart rate among members of your class?

Answers will vary but should directly relate to the actual class data.

7. Research to find information about the assessment of physical fitness and improving physical fitness. Write one to two paragraphs reflecting on your own physical fitness. Include data from this activity. Set a specific goal for yourself related to maintaining or improving your cardiovascular health.

Cooking with Bacteria

Purpose

Students will measure and compare the pH changes that occur in raw cabbage soaked in salt water and cooked cabbage soaked in salt water. They will find that the presence of bacteria on the cabbage is necessary for the chemical reaction that changes cabbage into sauerkraut.

Time Requirements

Preparation: 30 minutes
Measurement: 24 hours
Analysis and Cleanup: 30 minutes

Advance Preparation

• Lightly wash and shred the cabbage. Boil half of the cabbage for 15 minutes and allow it to cool in the cooking water prior to the lab. Sterilize the beakers and allow them to cool. All utensils used for the lab should be thoroughly cleaned and sterilized to prevent unwanted bacterial contamination.
• Load DataMate on the calculators.

Materials

• Two heads of cabbage should be sufficient for the entire class.
• Small jars can be used instead of the beakers but the jars should be identical in size.
• Because this is an extended lab, you will need to have each CBL 2 unit connected to an AC power adapter. See the manual that accompanies the CBL 2 unit for specifications.
• Install fresh batteries in the calculator and CBL 2 to ensure that data is collected in the event of a power outage.

Safety Information

• Remind students that they should never eat or drink any materials used in the lab.
• Have students review all safety precautions and laboratory rules.

Teaching Tips

• Review the pH scale with students. In this lab, students measure the level of acidity of a salt solution by monitoring its pH. You should expect the data obtained by students to vary greatly, but the general trend should clearly show that the pH drops very slowly for boiled cabbage and more quickly for raw cabbage.
• Be sure students understand that this lab involves fermentation. The chemical process of fermentation varies with different foods. In the production of sauerkraut, the cabbage is salted to draw out fluid. It is kept in an anaerobic environment to allow the anaerobic bacteria to produce lactic acid.
• The shape of the graph curve depends strongly on the preparation conditions. Have students compare their graphs and discuss the reasons for the differences.
• Stress that the purpose of this lab is to show that the presence of bacteria is essential for fermentation.

Teacher Preparation (continued)

Extensions

When the measurements are completed, students can prove that it was the presence of bacteria that produced the differences in acid production by looking at samples under a microscope. Have students prepare slides by using a toothpick to place very small scrapings of each type of cabbage on different slides. Stain the samples with methylene blue for better visibility. Remind students to use very clean slides and cover slips to avoid contaminating the samples.

Pre-Lab Answers

1. A specific strain of bacteria is responsible.

2. It will fall because the solution would become more acidic.

3. Boiling the cabbage kills the bacteria, resulting in less lactic acid produced.

4. The curve of the pH of raw cabbage would fall rapidly, but the curve of the pH of boiled cabbage would fall very slowly because it has fewer bacteria to produce lactic acid.

A sample graph of the pH changes in cooked and raw cabbage is shown below.

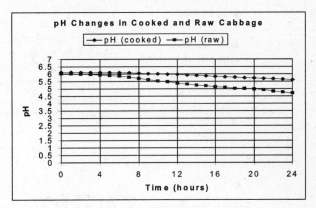

LAB 3 Probeware Activity

Cooking with Bacteria

Usually you think of bacteria as something that can make you sick. But some types of bacteria are useful in food preparation. When cabbage is salted and kept in a closed container, bacteria in the cabbage cause it to ferment and become sauerkraut. The salt kills some bacteria but the sauerkraut-producing bacteria on the cabbage survive. In this activity, you will conduct a 24-hour measurement to compare how fast lactic acid is produced during the fermentation of raw cabbage and cabbage that has been boiled.

What You'll Investigate

- How can bacteria help in food production?
- How does the amount of bacteria affect the rate of lactic acid production during the fermentation of cabbage?

Goals

Measure the change in pH during the fermentation of cabbage.
Hypothesize what is responsible for the production of lactic acid during the fermentation of cabbage.

Materials

CBL 2 or LabPro units (2)
TI graphing calculators (2)
link cable (2)
DataMate program
AC power adapters (2)
pH probes (2)
ring stand (2)
test-tube clamps (2)
250-mL beakers, sterilized (2)
400-mL beaker

wash bottle
glass stirring rod
shredded raw cabbage
shredded boiled cabbage
distilled water
tongs (2)
non-iodized salt
plastic food wrap
aluminum foil

Safety Precautions

- Always wear safety goggles and a lab apron.
CAUTION: Never eat lab materials.

Pre-Lab

1. In the production of sauerkraut, the natural sugar in cabbage is broken down into lactic acid and carbon dioxide. What organism is responsible for this process?

2. As lactic acid is produced during the fermentation process, will the pH of the cabbage solution rise or fall?

3. How would boiling the cabbage affect the amount of lactic acid that is produced?

4. Hypothesize how the graphs of pH would differ if you measure the pH change in raw cabbage placed in salt water and boiled cabbage placed in salt water.

Lab 3   9

Probeware Activity 3 (continued)

Procedure

Part A: Preparing the CBL System

1. Set up the calculator and CBL 2 units, as shown in **Figure 1**. Connect each CBL 2 unit to an AC power adapter. Plug each adapter into an outlet. Plug the pH probes into channel 1 of each CBL 2 unit. Turn on the calculators and start DataMate. Press CLEAR to reset the program. The pH probes should be recognized automatically. If not, turn to page *vi* for instructions on how to set up the probes manually.

Figure 1

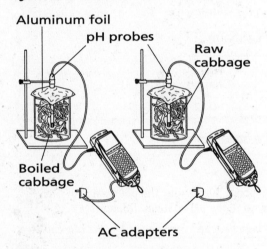

Aluminum foil
pH probes
Raw cabbage
Boiled cabbage
AC adapters

2. Select **SETUP.** Press the up arrow once until the cursor is beside the **MODE** line. Press ENTER.

3. Select **TIME GRAPH.** Then select **CHANGE TIME SETTINGS.** The calculator will ask you to input the time between samples in seconds. Press 1 8 0 0. Then press ENTER.

4. The calculator will ask you to enter the number of samples. Press 4 8. Then press ENTER.

5. Select **OK.** Then select **OK** again. The calculators and CBL 2 units are now ready to record pH readings every 1800 seconds (half hour) for 24 hours.

Part B: Collecting Data

1. Prepare a salt solution by mixing 10 g of salt in 400 mL of distilled water.

2. Using sterilized tongs, place boiled cabbage into one of the 250-mL beakers. Using another set of sterilized tongs, place raw cabbage into the other beaker. Fill both beakers to the 200-mL mark with cabbage. Then fill both beakers almost to the brim with salt solution.

3. Cover the beakers with plastic wrap, then with a square of aluminum foil. The plastic wrap and foil should have a small hole in the center to allow a pH probe to fit through it.

4. Remove the storage solution bottles from the pH probes. Slide the o-ring and cap up the sensor barrel, out of the way. Over a sink or empty beaker, use a wash bottle of distilled water to thoroughly rinse the probes. Attach the probes to the ring stand and place the ends of the probes in the solution in the beakers. Wrap extra foil around the end of the probe to keep the setup as clean as possible.

5. Wait a few minutes to allow the pH readings to stabilize. Select **START** on each calculator to begin the 24-hour measurements. A screen will appear that tells you to press "enter" to continue. Press ENTER. The calculators may be removed now. The CBL 2 units will continue collecting data.

6. After 24 hours, when the data collection is complete, reattach the calculators. Press ON to turn them on.

7. Start DataMate. A screen will appear reminding you that data has been collected. Press ENTER to go to the main screen. Select the **TOOLS** option. Select the **RETRIEVE DATA** option. A graph of the data should appear. Sketch and label the graphs in your **Science Journal.**

Probeware Activity 3 (continued)

Part C: Examining Data

1. For each graph, return to the main screen by pressing ENTER.

2. Select **ANALYZE.**

3. Select **STATISTICS.**

4. Press ENTER to select the beginning of the pH graph. Use the right arrow key to select the end of the pH graph. Press ENTER.

5. Your calculator will display the minimum and maximum pH values. Determine which of these is the initial pH and which is the final pH. Round these values to the hundredths place and record them in the **Data Table.**

6. When you are finished, press ENTER. Select **RETURN TO MAIN SCREEN.** Select **QUIT.** Follow directions on the screen.

Cleanup and Disposal

1. Remove the pH probes from the beakers of cabbage. Use distilled water in a wash bottle to rinse the probes thoroughly and place them in the storage-solution bottles.

2. Turn off the graphing calculators and disconnect the pH probes and CBL 2 units. Follow your teacher's instructions for disposing the contents of the beakers.

3. Clean and return all equipment as directed by your teacher.

Data Table: pH Changes of Raw and Cooked Cabbage

Type of Cabbage	Initial pH	Final pH	pH Change
Cooked	6.12	5.60	−0.52
Raw	6.03	4.71	−1.32

Conclude and Apply

1. Compare the pH graphs for the raw and boiled cabbage. Determine the pH change of each by subtracting the initial pH from the final pH. Why were the pH changes different?

   For the boiled cabbage, the pH was stable at first then dropped very slowly. For the raw cabbage,

   the pH dropped rapidly. Bacteria in the raw cabbage produced lactic acid, causing the pH to fall

   rapidly. The boiled cabbage had fewer bacteria, so its pH fell much slower.

2. Compare your results to your hypothesis in **Pre-Lab** question 4. Explain the source of any differences.

   Students may have thought the pH of the boiled cabbage wouldn't change at all.

   The pH drops slowly in the boiled cabbage because there was a smaller number of bacteria

   than in the raw cabbage.

Sweat is Cool

LAB 4 Teacher Preparation

Purpose

Students will observe the cooling process that occurs during the evaporation of two different liquids. Students will collect temperature data as the evaporation proceeds using a CBL 2 unit and a temperature probe. Data will be viewed and analyzed using a graphing calculator.

Time Requirements

one 45-minute class period

Advance Preparation

- Prepare student lab stations with the required materials at each location. This will enable students to begin working immediately.
- Allow at least 12 hours for the alcohol and tap water to reach room temperature before starting the lab. Fill large beakers with tap water the day before class. The students can use the water from this container for their lab. Make sure you have enough water for each class that day.

Safety Information

- Students should observe safe laboratory procedures and wear lab aprons and goggles during the entire lab.
- **CAUTION:** Extinguish all flames in the lab while students perform this activity. Isopropyl alcohol is flammable.
- Provide adequate ventilation during the activity.

Teaching Tips

- Prepare the CBL 2 system for the students by linking the graphing calculator and the CBL 2 unit. Make sure the DataMate program is loaded, the temperature probe is attached, and the system is ready to use.
- Students might not know *how* a liquid is cooled during evaporation. A liquid is made up of moving particles. Some particles are moving faster and, thus, have more kinetic energy than others. The temperature of a substance is the average kinetic energy of all the particles of a substance. The particles on a liquid exert attractive forces on each other. Near the surface of a liquid, some particles moving toward the surface are moving fast enough to break free of these attractive forces. These fast-moving particles will leave the liquid. The slower-moving particles will remain. The remaining particles have a lower average kinetic energy and, thus, a lower temperature.
- Review with students the role that skin plays in regulating body temperature. When blood vessels in the skin dilate, like during exercise, pores open in the skin and sweat moves out of them and onto the surface of the skin. As sweat evaporates, the remaining sweat on the skin becomes cooler. Since heat flows from a warmer object to a cooler one, heat from your warm skin moves to the cooler sweat on your skin. Your skin is cooled.

Teacher Preparation (continued)

Extensions

- Have students research how heat is transferred by conduction.
- Have students research how emotion and puberty can affect perspiration.
- Have students research how fever is both harmful and beneficial during an illness and what procedures can be used to reduce or increase body temperature.
- Have students research the causes of hyperhidrosis, or excessive perspiration.
- Have students research how cold-blooded mammals regulate body temperature.
- Assign the above topics to different students. Students can give an oral report to the class about their topic and share their information.

Pre-Lab Answers

1. During the evaporation of a liquid, heat is absorbed from the surroundings.

2. You could observe the change in temperature of the surroundings during evaporation.

3. Liquid on the surface of the skin absorbs heat from your body as it evaporates. The removal of heat from the body helps the body maintain a constant temperature.

4. Situations such as exercise, weather, puberty, illness, or stress can cause the rate of perspiration to change.

Sample evaporation graphs are shown below.

Graph of Water Sample Data

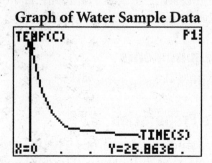

Graph of Alcohol Sample Data

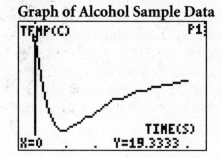

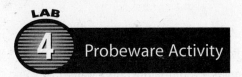

Sweat is Cool

The human body needs to maintain an internal body temperature of about 37°C to survive. When the body becomes too hot it begins to perspire, or sweat. Tiny sweat glands in the dermis layer of your skin secrete a fluid that contains water, salt, and wastes. This fluid absorbs heat from the body as it evaporates, cooling the body. In this lab you will observe how evaporation of a liquid is a cooling process.

What You'll Investigate

- Is heat removed from the environment during the evaporation of a liquid such as during perspiration?
- How can this loss of heat be observed?

Goals

Observe the temperature change as a liquid evaporates.
Interpret the data that is collected during the evaporation of a liquid.

Materials

CBL 2 or LabPro unit
TI graphing calculator
DataMate program
link cable
temperature probe
1/2 coffee filter
  *filter paper
  *cotton ball
  *cotton gauze
small rubber bands
250-mL beaker
electric fan
isopropyl alcohol

Alternate materials

Safety Precautions 🥼 🥽 ⚡ 🔥

- Always wear safety goggles and a lab apron during a laboratory activity.
- Possible danger from electrical shock. Clean up spills immediately.
- Extinguish all flames during this activity. Isopropyl alcohol is flammable.

Pre-Lab

1. Where does the heat energy needed for a liquid to evaporate come from?

2. What measurement can be observed that shows this heat transfer?

3. Explain how perspiring cools your body.

4. What are some situations that can cause your rate of perspiration to change?

Probeware Activity 4 (continued)

Procedure

Part A: Preparing the CBL System

1. Set up the calculator and CBL 2 unit, as shown in **Figure 1.** Plug the temperature probe into channel 1 of the CBL 2 unit.

Figure 1

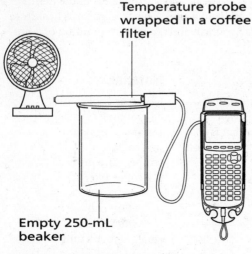

Temperature probe wrapped in a coffee filter

Empty 250-mL beaker

2. Turn on the calculator and start DataMate. Press CLEAR to reset the program. The temperature probe should be recognized automatically. If not, turn to page *vi* for instructions on how to set up the probe manually.

3. Select **SETUP** on the DataMate main screen to setup the time interval between data points and the length of time the data will be collected.

4. Press the up arrow once until the cursor is beside the **MODE** line. Press ENTER.

5. Select **TIME GRAPH.**

6. Select **CHANGE TIME SETTINGS.** The screen will display "Enter the time interval between samples in seconds." Press 1 5 ENTER. The screen will display "Enter number of samples." Press 4 0 ENTER. The CBL 2 unit will collect data every 15 seconds for 10 minutes (600 seconds). Select **OK** twice to exit. The setup screen appears.

Part B: Collecting Data

1. Using the room-temperature water that your teacher provides, put 50 mL of water into the 250-mL beaker.

2. Fold the coffee filter into a strip approximately 2 cm wide. Wrap it around the temperature probe and secure it with a small rubber band.

3. Wet the coffee filter by dipping it into your cup of water. Use care when wetting the filter and do not get water on your lab table. Wipe up spills immediately.

4. Place the probe across the top of an empty beaker, as shown in **Figure 1,** to support it during the experiment.

5. Place an electric fan 40 cm from your probe. Turn the fan on low and position the airflow so that it flows across the wetted filter.

6. Select **START** to begin collecting data.

Part C: Examining the Data

1. After data collection is complete, sketch and label the graph shown on the calculator screen in your **Science Journal.** Return to the main screen by pressing ENTER.

2. Select **ANALYZE.**

3. Select **STATISTICS.**

4. Press ENTER to select the beginning of the temperature graph. Use the right arrow key to select the final temperature. Press ENTER.

5. The calculator will display the minimum and maximum temperatures. Determine which of these is the initial temperature and which of these is the temperature after the liquid has evaporated—the final temperature. Record these in the **Data Table.**

6. Press ENTER. Select **RETURN TO THE MAIN SCREEN.**

7. Repeat parts B and, steps 1–5 of part C using isopropyl alcohol.

8. When you are finished, press ENTER. Select **RETURN TO THE MAIN SCREEN.** Select **QUIT.** Follow the directions on the screen.

14   Lab 4

Probeware Activity 4 (continued)

Cleanup and Disposal

1. Turn off the graphing calculator and disconnect the temperature probe and CBL 2 unit.
2. Put the solid waste into the container designated by your teacher.
3. Return all equipment to the proper location as directed by your teacher.

Data Table: Temperature Changes Due to Evaporation

	Initial Temperature	Final Temperature	Temperature Change
Water			
Alcohol			

Conclude and Apply

1. Find the temperature change for each substance by subtracting the initial temperature from the final temperature. Record your results in the **Data Table.**

2. What energy exchanges occurred during the evaporation process?

    The liquids absorbed thermal energy from the surrounding air, paper filter, and temperature

    probe during the evaporation process. The temperature of the surroundings decreased.

3. How is the evaporation process in this lab similar to perspiration in the human body? How is it different?

    Water and perspiration absorb heat from their surroundings as they evaporate resulting in a

    cooling effect. In this lab, we used water and isopropyl alcohol to simulate sweat but neither

    contain the salts and wastes that our perspiration contains..

4. Perspiration occurs under heavy clothing in cold temperatures. Why is it beneficial to wear undergarments that wick the moisture away from the surface of the skin?

    Removing the liquid from the surface of your skin reduces the amount of heat that is

    removed from your body as the liquid evaporates. This will help keep you warmer and

    more comfortable.

5. What differences do you observe in the time-temperature graphs for alcohol and water?

    The graph for water showed that the surrounding temperature decreased quickly and then more

    slowly. The graph for alcohol showed that the surrounding temperature decreased quickly and

    then began to increase (after the majority of the alcohol had evaporated).

Lab 4   15

Biodiversity and Ecosystems

LAB 5 Teacher Preparation

Purpose

Students will conduct a field investigation to learn about the environment. They will observe biotic and abiotic factors of an ecosystem. Students will use the CBL 2 and a temperature probe to collect data and a graphing calculator to display and analyze data.

Time Requirements

two 45-minute class periods—one for the field investigation and one for data analysis

Advance Preparation

- Select and visit the site. Check for hazards such as debris, poison ivy, steep terrain, or open water. Collect sample data to test the lab.
- Prior to the trip, mark site areas with stakes and letters. Estimate and record the biodiversity level (high, medium, or low) for each site.
- Divide students into groups, assign sites, and assign group members' well-defined responsibilities. Each group should collect data from two sites, each with a different level of biodiversity. Provide clipboards with attached pencils for data collection.
- Plan how you will carry and account for all equipment. Plastic tubs make excellent totes. Tape an index card inside the cover for your inventory. Count items three times—before you leave school, when you are ready to return from the site, and after you return to school.

- Wrap colorful plastic tape on your link cables.
- Precut lengths of string to mark off the square meter (about 4.5 m each).
- Bring extra batteries.
- Reset the memory on the calculators and transfer DataMate.
- Make transparencies of centimeter graph paper. Cut them into 10-cm × 10-cm grids, ten grids for each student group.
- Students can do much of this preparation as an extracurricular activity. Your school's ecology club, honor society, or tech-assistant program has young people that are eager to help. Use PTA volunteers, also.

Safety Information

- Ask students if they have outdoor allergies, such as reactions to bee stings. Take any needed medications along with a first-aid kit and emergency information.
- Review proper attire for fieldwork such as sturdy shoes, socks, pants, and a hat. A fanny pack or small backpack with a water bottle is a good idea. Bug repellent and sunscreen are often needed.
- If available, take along a cell phone.

Teaching Tips

- Observing nature requires patience and practice. Provide students with at least one opportunity before this lab to go outside and quietly observe. Allow them to record their observations in any way they choose— a simple list, a drawing, watercolor, poetry, narrative, etc. Students should be encouraged to share their creations. Differentiate qualitative from quantitative observations and discuss advantages and disadvantages of these two types of data.

Teacher Preparation (continued)

- Familiarize students with how to identify some local plants and insects. Bring along field guides for accurate identification.
- Define humus and show students a soil profile (or a picture of one) so they can see that humus is on top of other soil layers.
- Model laying out a one-meter square, marking it with string and sticks.
- Demonstrate the 10-cm × 10-cm transparency method for counting plant types in the field.
- Ask the math teacher to team with you or have his or her students practice converting from fractions to percentages, calculating averages, and constructing circle graphs.

Extensions

- Investigate Project Globe, an international environmental data effort sponsored by the National Oceanic and Atmospheric Administration (NOAA). This is an opportunity for student data, such as local temperature and land cover descriptions, to be used by scientists worldwide.
- Students are expected to use computers to organize information and to construct tables and graphs. Show students how to use a spreadsheet program with charting capabilities to produce both the circle graph and the scatter plot. Students can produce a lab report using a word processing program and insert their graphs and plots generated with the spreadsheet program.

Pre-Lab Answers

1. Possible answers: various types of grasses, weeds, snails, earthworms, and grub worms

2. Possible answers: rabbits, birds, squirrels, and snakes

3. Possible answers: temperature, soil pH, humidity, wind speed, and barometric pressure

4. Possible answers: use a tool such as a thermometer, a pH meter, or wind speed indicator

A sample circle graph of a site with a low level of biodiversity is shown below.

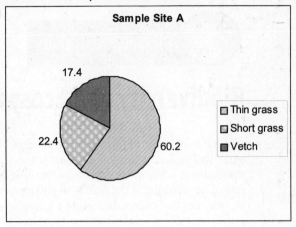

A sample circle graph of a site with a high level of biodiversity is shown below.

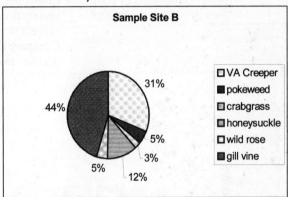

A sample graph of temperature versus height above ground is shown below.

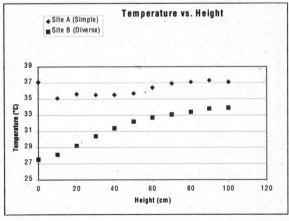

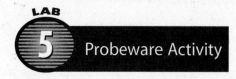

Biodiversity and Ecosystems

What lives in your home or on your school lawn? What lives in the wooded areas at the local park? You probably have noticed that some organisms' habitats include both a grassland and a wooded area while other organisms live only in one type of area. In this activity you will play the role of an ecologist in the field. You will observe plant and animal organisms at two different sample sites and collect data using a graphing calculator and a temperature probe.

What You'll Investigate

- What plants and animals live in two ecosystems?
- What is the effect of plant diversity on temperature?

Goals

Observe living organisms in a measured area.
Count the plant types observed using percentages.
Collect temperature data.
Compare the temperature data for two different sites.

Materials

CBL 2 or LabPro unit
TI graphing calculator
link cable
DataMate program
temperature probe
meterstick
string
8 wooden dowels or craft sticks
10 acetate grids (10 cm × 10 cm)
colored transparency markers
trowel
drawing compass
protractor

Safety Precautions 🐀 ☠

CAUTION: Do not touch or harass animals in the field. Do not eat any fruits, berries, or plant material from the site. Beware of poisonous and thorny plants.

Pre-Lab

1. Predict the type of living organisms you might find in a small plot of lawn.

2. Predict the types of animals you might find in a small plot with more diverse vegetation.

3. List any abiotic factors you could observe at a small site in the field.

4. Describe how you could measure one of the abiotic factors.

Lab 5 **17**

Probeware Activity 5 (continued)

Procedure

Part A: Collecting Plant and Animal Data

1. At your assigned site, measure a one-meter square area and mark it with string and sticks as demonstrated by your teacher.

2. Examine your area carefully. Count the different types of plants. Look for any animals or signs of animal life. Record your observations in **Data Table 1.** You do not need to know the exact name of the plants and animals, but include measurements. A description such as "short (4 cm), thin, yellowish-green grass" is acceptable.

3. Use a trowel to carefully lift out a section of soil. Describe how much effort was needed to remove the soil. Observe the humus layer and record its depth in **Data Table 1.** Replace the soil.

4. Randomly lay five of your 10-cm × 10-cm acetate grids on the ground within your square meter, as shown in **Figure 1.**

5. Using transparency markers, code each small square with a color, number, or symbol to represent the type of plant visible within that square.

6. Repeat steps 1–5 for your second assigned site.

Figure 1

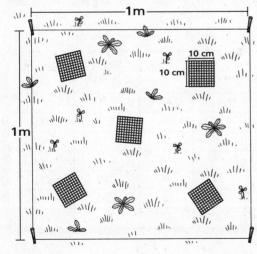

Part B: Collecting Temperature Data

1. Plug the temperature probe into channel 1 of the CBL 2.

2. Turn on the graphing calculator and start DataMate. Press CLEAR to reset the program. The temperature probe should be recognized automatically. If not, turn to page *vi* for instructions on how to set up the probe manually.

3. To investigate the effect of height above the ground on temperature, stand a meterstick in the middle of your sample site. Place the "zero" end on the ground.

4. Put the temperature probe on the ground next to the meterstick. The temperature reading is located in the upper right-hand corner of the calculator screen. Allow enough time for the temperature reading to stabilize. After 30 seconds have passed, record the temperature in **Data Table 3.**

5. Move the probe to the 10-cm mark and repeat the procedure. Measure and record the temperature at each 10-cm increment. Your last reading will be at 100 cm.

6. Repeat steps 1–5 for your second assigned site.

7. After all of your data is collected, select **QUIT.** Follow the directions on the calculator screen.

Cleanup and Disposal

1. Turn off the calculator and disconnect the temperature probe and CBL 2.

2. Return all lab materials to the appropriate location as directed by your teacher.

3. Collect personal belongings and pick up any trash at your site.

Copyright © Glencoe/McGraw-Hill, a division of the McGraw-Hill Companies, Inc.

Probeware Activity 5 (continued)

Data Table 1: Soil Conditions and Organisms

	Site A	Site B
Plants found	1. short (4 cm), thin yellowish green grass 2. taller (10 cm), thick dark green grass 3. vetch with tiny pink flowers	1. Virginia creeper 2. pokeweed 3. crabgrass 4. honeysuckle 5. wild rose 6. gill o' the ground
Animals/Animal signs found	1. tiny white hopper 2. two ant hills, no ants visible	1. worms 2. honey bees 3. beetle 4. pill bugs 5. bird in overhanging tree
Depth of humus (cm)	0.5	12
Ease of penetrating ground	hard to dig in	very easy, like soft butter

Data Table 2A: Plant Analysis at Site A

Plant Type	Number of Squares out of 100					Total (of 500)	Percent (%)
	Grid 1	Grid 2	Grid 3	Grid 4	Grid 5		
1. thin grass	58	62	65	56	60	301	60.2
2. short grass	25	20	30	19	18	112	22.4
3. vetch	17	18	5	25	22	87	17.4

Data Table 2B: Plant Analysis at Site B

Plant Type	Number of Squares out of 100					Total (of 500)	Percent (%)
	Grid 1	Grid 2	Grid 3	Grid 4	Grid 5		
1. Virginia creeper	35	25	26	37	33	156	31.2
2. pokeweed	0	0	0	0	24	24	4.8
3. crabgrass	10	0	0	3	0	13	2.6
4. honeysuckle	0	10	12	20	16	58	11.6
5. wild rose	8	5	10	0	0	23	4.6
6. gill o' the ground	47	60	52	40	27	226	45.2

Lab 5   **19**

Probeware Activity 5 (continued)

Data Table 3: Temperature vs. Height

Height (cm)	Temperature (°C)	
	Site A	Site B
0	37.1	27.5
10	35.1	28.1
20	35.6	29.2
30	35.5	30.4
40	35.5	31.4
50	35.7	32.2
60	36.5	32.7
70	36.9	33.1
80	37.1	33.4
90	37.3	33.8
100	37.1	33.9

Part C: Analyzing Data

1. Count the number of small squares for each plant type and record it in **Data Table 2A** or **2B**. Convert the total count from the five grids to percentages.

2. Construct two circle graphs to compare the plant percentages for Site A and Site B. If you have a TI-73 your teacher may want you to make your circle graphs on the graphing calculator. See **Appendix E** for directions.

3. Construct a graph that shows the relationship between temperature and height for each site. Place the independent variable on the *x*-axis and the dependent variable on the *y*-axis. Include a key.

Conclude and Apply

1. Compare the diversity of organisms in your two ecosystems. List at least two similarities and three differences between Site A and Site B. Be specific.

   Answers will vary. For sample data, the site with sparse vegetation has three types of plants and two

   types of animals. The site with a large amout of vegetation has six types of plants and five types of

   animals. Both sites contained plants and animals and have the same climate. The sites differ in amount

   and types of plants and animals, as well as soil type.

2. In your temperature-height graph, what was your independent variable? What was your dependent (responding) variable? Why does the graph need a key?

   The independent variable was the height above ground. The dependent variable was temperature. A key

   is needed to distinguish the data from the two sites.

3. Describe any differences in the temperature vs. height at Sites A and B. Explain how this factor might affect the plants and animals found there.

   Answers will vary, but should reflect the data collected. For the site with sparse vegetation, the tempera-

   ture was almost ten degrees higher than the site with more diverse vegetation, which would limit the

   plants that could live there. The site with diverse vegetation provides more food, moisture, shelter, and

   nesting spots than the sparse site.

LAB 6 Teacher Preparation

The Effect of Acid Rain on Limestone

Purpose

Students will collect rainwater and measure its acidity. They will use the rainwater to determine the effect that acid rain has on limestone.

Time Requirements

one 45-minute class period

Advance Preparation

- Crush limestone into small, pea-sized pieces. Each student will need about five pieces.
- Install the DataMate program on the graphing calculators.

Materials

The rainwater in this activity should have a pH of about 3.5 or lower. If necessary, students can prepare simulated acid rain with a pH of about 3.5 by adding 1.5 mL of vinegar to 100 mL of distilled water.

Safety Information

Remind students to review all safety precautions and to observe laboratory rules.

Teaching Tips

- Before the lab, review the meaning of pH with students. Be sure they understand that pH is logarithmic. A solution with a pH of 3, for example, is ten times more acidic than a solution with a pH of 4.
- Discuss acid rain and how it affects limestone. Show students limestone rocks.
- Explain that limestone is composed mainly of calcite (calcium carbonate), a crystal that is dissolved easily by acid rain.
- Bring in an antacid package. Tell students that calcium carbonate is a primary ingredient in many antacids because of its ability to neutralize acids.

Extensions

Students can investigate how the level of acidity of acid rain affects limestone by repeating the experiment using simulated rainwater with different pH values. Add enough vinegar to distilled water to prepare solutions with pH values of 2.5, 3.5, 4.5, and 5.5. Have them repeat the experiment for each of these solutions and compare the results. Students also can collect rainwater over an extended period and determine if the acidity changes over time.

Pre-Lab Answers

1. The pH scale is a measure of acidity. A substance with a pH of 7 is neutral. A substance with pH less than 7 is acidic, and a substance with pH greater than 7 is basic.

2. less acidic

3. The solution would become less acidic and the pH would rise.

4. A solution with a pH of 3 is ten times more acidic than a solution with a pH of 4.

A sample graph is shown below.

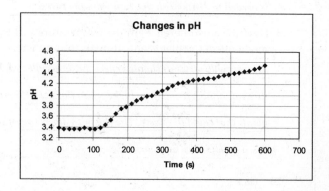

LAB 6 Probeware Activity

The Effect of Acid Rain on Limestone

Acid rain is harming some of the world's most beautiful structures. Ancient Mayan pyramids in Mexico are crumbling because the acidic rainwater slowly dissolves minerals in the rocks. The Taj Mahal in India has undergone extensive and costly reconstruction to repair damage from acid rain. Buildings and monuments in Washington, D.C. are slowly weathering because precipitation in the area is ten times more acidic than unpolluted rainwater. In this activity, you will observe the effect that acid rain has on limestone. Limestone is the type of rock that was used in the construction of many of the damaged structures. It is composed primarily of calcite (calcium carbonate), a mineral that is dissolved easily by weak acids.

What You'll Investigate

- What is the pH of rain in your area?
- How does the pH of acid rain change when limestone is added to it?
- What effect does acid rain have on limestone?

Goals

Measure the pH of rainwater.
Observe the effect that limestone has on the pH of acid rain.
Infer the effect that acid rain has on limestone buildings and monuments.

Materials

CBL 2 or LabPro unit
TI graphing calculator
link cable
DataMate program
pH probe
150-mL beaker
400-mL beaker
distilled water
1-L glass jar
pea-sized limestone
  pebbles (5)

Safety Precautions 👓 🧤

- Always wear safety goggles and a lab apron.

Pre-Lab

1. Explain the pH scale.
2. If the pH of an acidic solution rises, does this indicate that the solution is becoming more acidic or less acidic?
3. What effect would adding a basic substance have on the pH of an acidic solution?
4. The pH scale is logarithmic. How does a pH of 3 compare to a pH of 4?

Lab 6   21

Probeware Activity 6 (continued)

Procedure

Part A: Preparing the CBL System

1. Place a glass jar outside, away from trees and buildings, during a rain shower. Collect at least 100 mL of rainwater. Cover the jar until you are ready to use it.

2. Connect the pH probe into channel 1 of the CBL 2 unit, as shown in **Figure 1**. Connect the CBL 2 unit to the graphing calculator.

Figure 1

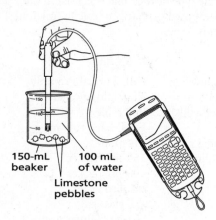

150-mL beaker   100 mL of water

Limestone pebbles

3. Turn on the graphing calculator and start the DataMate program. Press [CLEAR] to reset the program. The pH probe should be recognized automatically. If not, turn to page *vi* for instructions on how to set up the probe manually.

4. Select **SETUP**. Press the up arrow once to select **MODE: TIMEGRAPH**. Press [ENTER].

5. Select **TIME GRAPH**. Select **CHANGE TIME SETTINGS**. The screen will display "Enter the time interval between samples in seconds."

6. Press [1] [5] [ENTER].

7. The screen will display "Enter number of samples." Press [4] [0] [ENTER]. The CBL 2 unit will collect data every 15 seconds for 10 minutes. Select **OK** twice.

Part B: Collecting Data

1. Partially fill a 400-mL beaker with distilled water. This will be the soaking solution.

2. Carefully unscrew the pH sensor from the storage-solution bottle sliding the cap and o-ring up the barrel of the sensor. Set the storage bottle aside. Over a sink, rinse the sensor with distilled water and place it in the soaking solution.

3. Pour 100 mL of rainwater into a 150-mL beaker. Insert the pH probe and watch the pH reading at the top right of the calculator screen. When the reading has stabilized, select **START**.

4. Gently swirl the pH probe in the rainwater. After about 2 minutes, add the limestone pebbles to the rainwater.

5. Gently swirl the pH probe until the recording period ends. Remember that the probe is fragile. Be sure the recording tip remains submerged but do not allow it to hit the pebbles or the side of the beaker.

6. At the end of 10 minutes, the CBL 2 unit will make a tone. Remove the pH probe from the rainwater, rinse it over a sink, and place it in the soaking solution.

7. Sketch and label your graph in the space below.

22   Lab 6

Probeware Activity 6 (continued)

Part C: Examining the Data

1. Observe the graph, noting what happened to the graph when the limestone was added.

2. Determine the initial pH of the rainwater before the limestone was added.

   a. Return to the main screen by pressing [ENTER]. Select **ANALYZE.** Select **STATISTICS.**

   b. Press [ENTER] to select the beginning of the graph.

   c. Use the right arrow key to select a point just before the limestone was added. Press [ENTER].

   d. Record the mean, which is the initial pH, in the **Data Table.** Press [ENTER].

3. Determine the pH after adding the limestone pebbles.

   a. Select **RETURN TO THE MAIN SCREEN.** Select **GRAPH.**

   b. Use the right arrow to select the last point on the graph. In the table below, record the y-value shown in the lower right corner of the screen. This is the final pH.

4. When you are finished with the graph, press [ENTER]. Select **QUIT.**

Data Table: pH Change	
Initial pH	3.3
Final pH	4.6
pH Change	1.3

Cleanup and Disposal

1. Remove the pH probe from the soaking beaker. Carefully place it in the storage-solution bottle.

2. Turn off the calculator and disconnect the pH probe and CBL 2 unit.

3. Follow your teacher's instructions for disposing of the contents of the beakers and returning all equipment to its proper location.

Conclude and Apply

1. Look at the graph of your data. What was the approximate time (x) when you added the limestone? How can you tell?

   Answers will vary. In the sample data, the limestone was added at about $x = 120$ s. A short time

   later, the pH of the solution began to rise.

2. Why did the graph change after you added the limestone? Calculate the change in pH.

   The acid began to dissolve the calcium carbonate in the limestone. The acidity of the rainwater decreased. Students

   should subtract the initial pH from the final pH.

3. What would you expect your graph to look like if you continued taking data for 10 additional minutes? How would this affect your final pH and the change in pH? How could you test this?

   Students might expect the pH to continue rising and eventually level off. The final pH would be higher than the

   value they recorded, and the pH change would be greater. They could test this by repeating the experiment using

   the same amount of limestone and water but allowing it to continue for 20 minutes.

4. Infer from your experiment how acid rain would affect a monument made of limestone.

   Students should infer that acid rain would gradually dissolve the calcite in the monument, eventually damaging it.

LAB 7 Teacher Preparation

The Formation of Caves

Purpose

Students will learn how caves form when rainwater becomes acidic as it combines with carbon dioxide from the atmosphere and soil and then dissolves rock. They will use a probe to monitor the pH of water as they exhale into it with a straw, increasing the amount of carbon dioxide. By analyzing a graph showing changes in the water's acidity, students will understand the process that forms caves.

Time Requirements

one 45-minute class period

Advance Preparation

- Install the DataMate program on the graphing calculators.
- Check pH probes. If calibration is necessary, refer to the probe manual.

Safety Information

- This lab requires students to exhale through a straw for 30 seconds. Make sure students do not have a medical condition, such as asthma, that would prevent them from safely performing this activity.
- Under no circumstances should students use a straw that someone else has already used.
- Review all safety precautions in the lab and remind them to observe all laboratory rules.

Teaching Tips

- Lead students in a discussion about the definition of an acid. According to one definition, it is a substance that produces hydrogen ions in water.

- Prior to the lab, lead students in a discussion of the pH scale.
- Explain that several geological processes can form caves. This lab focuses on solution caves, formed when water rich in carbon dioxide seeps into cracks in carbonate rocks such as limestone. Water combines with carbon dioxide to form carbonic acid, which reacts with limestone.

$$H_2O + CO_2 \rightarrow H_2CO_3$$

$$H_2CO_3 + CaCO_3 \rightarrow 2HCO_3^- + Ca^{2+}$$

Extensions

Have students research how stalactites and stalagmites form in caves. Students can prepare a short report to present to the class.

Pre-Lab Answers

1. Rainwater becomes acidic as it combines with carbon dioxide from the atmosphere and soil. This acidic rainwater dissolves rock.

2. A substance with a pH greater than 7 is a base. A substance with a pH of 7 is neutral. A substance with a pH less than 7 is an acid.

3. The acidity has increased.

4. The acidity of the water would increase because carbon dioxide in your breath would combine with the water to form carbonic acid.

A sample graph of the pH change is shown below.

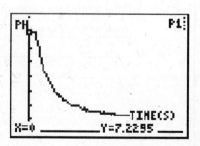

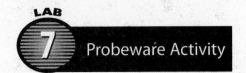

Probeware Activity

The Formation of Caves

Many processes form caves. Powerful waves carve sea caves in rocks located next to the ocean. Lava flowing from volcanoes forms caves if the surface lava cools and hardens before the lava underneath stops flowing. The most common type of cave forms when underground layers of rock, such as limestone, are dissolved by acidic groundwater. In this process, rainwater absorbs carbon dioxide as it falls through the air. As the water seeps through the ground, it absorbs more carbon dioxide in soil pores. The rainwater becomes acidic because water and carbon dioxide form a weak acid known as carbonic acid. When this acidic water reaches bedrock, it seeps through cracks, dissolving the rock and creating open areas. Slowly, over many thousands of years, the water creates a cave in the rock. In this activity, you will demonstrate the effect of increasing the amount of carbon dioxide in water. The carbon dioxide in your breath will react with the water, similar to the way rainwater reacts with carbon dioxide as it falls to Earth and seeps through the soil.

What You'll Investigate

- How does an increase in carbon dioxide affect the acidity of water?
- How does the acidity of water lead to the formation of caves?

Goals

Predict how increasing the carbon dioxide in water will affect its acidity.

Measure the change in acidity of water as you exhale into it.

Analyze a graph to determine what chemical change has taken place.

Materials

CBL 2 or LabPro unit
TI graphing calculator
link cable
DataMate program
pH probe
timer
distilled water
600-mL beaker
wash bottle
plastic drinking straw

Safety Precautions

- Always wear safety goggles and a lab apron.

Pre-Lab

1. Describe how rainwater can contribute to the formation of a cave.

2. Describe how the pH scale is used to determine whether a substance is basic or acidic.

3. Suppose you determine that a substance has a pH of 6. An hour later, it has a pH of 2. Has the acidity of the substance increased or decreased?

4. Predict how exhaling through a straw into water would affect the acidity of the water. Explain your answer.

Lab 7 25

Probeware Activity 7 (continued)

Procedure

Part A: Preparing the CBL System

1. Set up the calculator and CBL 2 unit, as shown in **Figure 1.** Plug the pH probe into channel 1 of the CBL 2 unit. Turn on the calculator and start DataMate. Press `CLEAR` to reset the program. The pH probe should be recognized automatically. If not, turn to page *vi* for instructions on how to set up the probe manually.

Figure 1

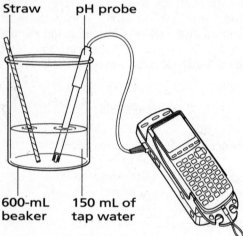

Straw   pH probe

600-mL beaker   150 mL of tap water

2. Select **Setup.** Press the up arrow once until the cursor is beside the **MODE** line. Press `ENTER`.

3. Select **TIME GRAPH.** Then select **CHANGE SETTINGS.** The calculator will ask you to input the time between seconds. Press `5` `ENTER`.

4. The calculator will ask you for the number of samples. Press `1` `2` `0` `ENTER`.

5. Select **OK.** Then select **OK** again. One pH reading will be collected every 5 seconds for 600 seconds (10 minutes).

Part B: Collecting Data

1. Put 150 mL of tap water into the 600-mL beaker.

2. Remove the pH probe from the storage-solution bottle. Slide the cap and o-ring up the barrel of the probe to move them out of the way. Over a sink or empty beaker, use distilled water in a wash bottle to thoroughly rinse the probe. Set the solution bottle aside in a location where it will not be disturbed. Place the pH probe in the 600-mL beaker.

3. Allow the pH probe to remain in the water for one minute until the readings stabilize. During this time you will be able to see the pH reading on the top right corner of the calculator screen.

4. Be sure the timer is set to count up. Select **START** on the calculator to begin the 10-minute measurement. When you hear the tone indicating the measurement is beginning, start the timer.

5. When 30 seconds have passed, use the straw to exhale into the water for 30 seconds. Cup your hands over the beaker as you exhale to ensure that water doesn't splash out onto the calculator. Do not try to exhale continuously. Inhale through your nose and exhale through the straw at a natural pace.

6. After exhaling for 30 seconds, allow the pH probe to remain in the water, undisturbed for the remainder of the 10-minute measurement.

7. A graph showing changes in the water's pH during the measurement period will appear on the calculator screen. Sketch and label this graph in your Science Journal.

8. Use the right and left arrow keys to move the cursor along the data points. The time (x) and the corresponding pH (y) values will appear at the bottom of the screen. Write the selected values in the **Data Table.**

9. When you are finished, press `ENTER`. Select **QUIT.** Follow the directions on the screen.

Probeware Activity 7 (continued)

Data Table: Selected pH Values

Time (s)	pH
0	
100	
200	
300	
400	
500	
600	

Cleanup and Disposal

1. Turn off the graphing calculator and disconnect the pH probe and the CBL 2 unit. Rinse the end of the probe with distilled water and place the probe in the storage-solution bottle.

2. Follow your teacher's instructions for disposing of the contents of the beakers and returning all equipment to proper locations.

Conclude and Apply

1. Describe and explain what your graph looks like between 0 and 30 seconds.

During the first 30 seconds, the line is horizontal because the pH didn't change.

2. Describe and explain the curve of your graph after 30 seconds.

Answers will vary. The graph should show a sharp drop at 30 seconds in response to exhaling in the water. This occurs because the carbon dioxide combines with water to form carbonic acid. The pH levels off when most of the carbon dioxide has reacted with the water.

3. Explain how the results you obtained in this activity are similar to what happens when caves form.

In this activity, exhaling into water added carbon dioxide which caused the water's acidity to increase. Similarly, when rainwater falls through the atmosphere and then seeps through soil, it absorbs carbon dioxide which increases its acidity. This acidic water dissolves underground rock, forming caves.

Measuring Earthquakes

Purpose

Students will learn how earthquake magnitudes are measured by creating a model seismograph. They will use a current probe to monitor the movement of a swinging magnet in a coiled wire. The shaking of a table will model the movements of the ground during an earthquake. By recording variations in the current, they will produce a graph of the movement of a shaking table.

Time Requirements

one 45-minute class period

Advance Preparation

- Choose locations where students may set up their seismographs.
- The model seismograph must sit on a table or chair that can move so that it can record the movement of a table or chair.
- To save class time, you may wish to pre-cut the wire to the correct length and strip the coating from the ends.
- Be sure the DataMate program is installed on the graphing calculators.

Materials

- The magnets used for this activity must be strong to obtain good data. An inexpensive method is to use ceramic disc magnets placed side-to-side to form a cylinder. About 25 to 30 discs will be needed for each setup.
- A strong cardboard or plastic tube, about 10 cm long with a 3-cm inner diameter is needed for each model seismograph.

- Students often have trouble producing a good wire coil. Cardboard tubes can be used for the core if they are strong, but the wire might easily slip as students are winding it. One solution is to use a replacement cover for a small paint roller. A typical trim roller replacement is a plastic cylinder, about 10 cm long. The fuzzy covering on the roller prevents the wire from slipping as the student makes the coil, and the inner diameter of the cylinder is wide enough to allow the magnet to freely swing inside.

Safety Information

Remind students to review all safety precautions in the lab and to observe laboratory rules.

Teaching Tips

- Students should work in small groups to create the model seismographs. Encourage them to repeat measurements to observe how various types of movement affect their graphs.
- It isn't necessary for students to completely understand electromagnetic induction in order to perform this activity, but they should realize that the movement of the magnet in the coil produces a current. Remind them that the magnetic field around a bar magnet is strongest near the ends, so a stronger current is induced if the magnet moves near one side of the coil rather than all the way through it.
- Remind students that there are various types of seismographs. In this activity they will model just one type.
- If you would like to pre-measure lengths of wire, be sure to measure them using a tube with the same diameter that the students will be using.

Teacher Preparation (continued)

Extensions

In actual seismographs, vertical movement is measured in additional to horizontal movement. Have students work in groups to develop a model seismograph that will simultaneously measure horizontal and vertical movement. If they have difficulty developing an idea of their own, you might suggest that they suspend a magnet from a spring so that it hangs down into a wire coil attached to a current probe.

Pre-Lab Answers

1. Possible answers: to determine an earthquake's magnitude, to determine the epicenter of an earthquake, to learn more about Earth's inner structure

2. A seismograph is an instrument that measures Earth's movement during an earthquake.

3. A current can be produced in a coiled wire by moving the magnet in and out of the center of the coiled wire.

A sample graph of model seismograph data is shown below.

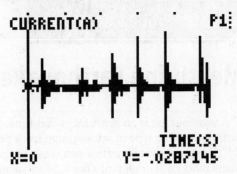

Measuring Earthquakes

A seismograph is an instrument that is used to measure the ground's movement during an earthquake. One type of seismograph has a pen attached to a pendulum. During an earthquake, a roll of paper moves beneath a pen creating lines that correspond to the motion of the ground. Many modern seismographs use a freely swinging magnet. The magnet is positioned inside a casing surrounded by coiled wire. When the ground moves, the casing moves relative to the magnet. Recall that a magnet is surrounded by a magnetic field. If a magnet moves in the coil, the magnetic field moves, and a current is generated in the wire. By measuring how this current changes, seismologists obtain a record of the ground's movement. In this activity, you will create a model seismograph with a magnet and coiled wire.

What You'll Investigate

- What is a seismograph?
- How does a seismograph register motion during an earthquake?
- What do the lines on a seismogram indicate about the strength of seismic waves?

Goals

Build a model seismograph.
Observe how a seismograph records motion.
Measure movement using a seismograph.
Create a seismogram.

Materials

CBL 2 or LabPro unit
TI graphing calculator
DataMate program
link cable
current probe
strong bar magnet
enameled copper magnet wire
cardboard or plastic tube
sandpaper
masking tape
ruler
string
table
chair

Safety Precautions

- Wear safety goggles and an apron during the lab.

Pre-Lab

1. What are some reasons why seismologists measure Earth's movement during an earthquake?

2. What is a seismograph?

3. How can you use a magnet to produce a current in a coiled wire?

Probeware Activity 8 (continued)

Procedure

Part A: Preparing the CBL System

1. Connect the current probe to channel 1 of the CBL 2 unit, as shown in **Figure 1.**

Figure 1

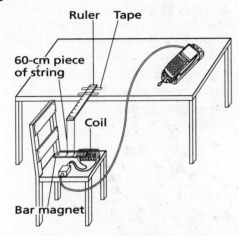

2. Use a link cable to connect the CBL 2 unit to the graphing calculator. Turn on the graphing calculator. Start the DataMate program. Press CLEAR to reset the program. The current probe should be recognized automatically. If not, turn to page *vi* for instructions on how to set up the probe manually.

3. Select **SETUP.** Press the up arrow once until the cursor is beside the **MODE: TIME GRAPH** line. Press ENTER.

4. Select **TIME GRAPH.** Select **CHANGE TIME SETTINGS.** The calculator will display "Enter time between samples in seconds." Press 0 . 2 ENTER.

5. The calculator will display "Enter number of samples." Press 1 2 0 ENTER.

6. Select **OK.** Select **OK** again. The calculator and CBL 2 unit are now ready to record changes in the current every 0.2 seconds for 24 seconds.

Part B: Collecting Data

1. To create a model seismograph, first make a coil of wire. Starting at one end of a sturdy tube, begin winding the wire securely around it, leaving about 20 cm of wire free at the beginning. Do not cut the wire from the spool until you have completed making the coil. Tape the wire at the place where you begin so it won't unwind. The windings should be close together. Make at least 50 windings before you get to the other end of the tube. Tape the wire at the end, leaving about 20 cm of wire free.

2. Use sandpaper to completely strip the coating off the ends of the wire. The coating on the wire doesn't conduct electricity, so it must be removed to ensure a good connection to the current probe. Be careful when doing this so that the coil does not unwind.

3. Connect each of the stripped ends of the wire coming from your wire coil to the red and black connectors of the current probe.

4. Cut a 60-cm piece of string. Tie each end around the ends of the bar magnet and slide the knots near the center of the magnet until they are about 2 cm apart. Tape the ruler to a table so that one end hangs over the edge. Use the string to hang the magnet from the ruler, as shown in **Figure 1.**

5. Tape your wire coil to the seat of a chair placed near the table. Position it so that the magnet swings freely through the end of the coil. You may have to adjust the length of the magnet's string by wrapping the string around the magnet.

Probeware Activity 8 (continued)

6. You are now ready to record movement with your seismograph. Select **START** to begin the 24-second measurement.

7. During this time, gently bump the table that suspends the magnet so that the magnet moves in and out of the wire coil. Allow it to stop moving, then bump it again. Do this repeatedly until the measurement period ends.

8. At the end of the measurement period, a graph of the movement will appear on the graphing calculator screen. Sketch and label the graph in your **Science Journal.** Use the graph to answer questions in the **Conclude and Apply** section. If you wish to repeat the measurement, press ENTER . Then select **START** again.

9. When you are finished, press ENTER . Select **RETURN TO MAIN SCREEN.** Select **QUIT.** Follow the directions on the screen.

Cleanup and Disposal

1. Turn off the graphing calculator and disconnect the CBL 2 unit and current probe. Disconnect the current probe wires from the wire coil. Remove the ruler from the table and the coil from the chair.

2. Dispose of or recycle the lab materials as directed by your teacher.

3. Return all equipment as directed by your teacher.

Conclude and Apply

1. To what do the up-and-down lines and the flat parts on the graph correspond?

   The up-and-down lines correspond to movement of the table, and the flat parts correspond to

   times when there was no movement.

2. How do you think your graph would differ if you had shaken the table harder? How does this relate to what a real seismogram shows about seismic waves?

   The up-and-down lines on the graph would have been higher if the motion of the table had

   been stronger. On a real seismogram, higher lines indicate stronger seismic waves.

3. In this lab, your wire coil remained still and the magnet moved inside it. In a real seismograph, the magnet remains still and the wire coil moves around it, even though the magnet can swing freely and the coil is attached firmly to the ground. Explain how this can be true.

   In a real seismogram, the ground is moving so the coil attached to it moves. The magnet doesn't

   move with the ground because it can swing freely.

4. Would you have obtained a similar or a different seismogram if you had moved the chair instead of the table? Explain.

   You would obtain a similar seismogram. It doesn't matter whether the magnet or the wire-coil

   moves. It is their movement relative to one another that causes the magnetic field to change

   and produces a current in the wire.

Predicting the Weather

Purpose

Students will use a relative-humidity sensor, barometer, and temperature probe to gather data about the weather over a five-day period. They will make daily observations of clouds, precipitation, and wind. At the end of the measurement period, they will compare their data with their weather observations and note any correlations.

Time Requirements

- one 30-minute class period to set up the weather station
- five minutes a day for five days to make weather observations
- 45-minute class period to analyze data

Advance Preparation

- Arrange space in the classroom where the weather stations can remain undisturbed throughout the measuring period. The CBL 2 units will need to be near an outlet.
- Obtain cloud charts and Beaufort wind scales for students to use.
- Install the DataMate program on the graphing calculators.
- Install fresh batteries in the calculators and CBL units to ensure that the CBL units continue to collect data in the event of a power outage.

Safety Information

- Have students review all safety precautions and laboratory rules.
- Make sure students don't make outside measurements when dangerous weather conditions exist.

Teaching Tips

- Have students begin their measurements a day or two before strong storms are expected. Although most of the weather observations will be made during students' regular class time, encourage them to stop by at other times to record observations in the weather log.
- The temperature and relative-humidity probes should be placed in a secure area away from direct sunlight and rain. The relative-humidity sensor must not get wet. One possible location is a windowsill, provided that it is shaded from sun and rain and that the cables connecting the probes to the CBL 2 unit will not be damaged when the window is closed.
- If a suitable location is not available, students can perform the activity by using only the barometer, or by taking temperature and relative humidity measurements only during school hours, when the probes can be monitored.
- This lab can be performed as a class project and only one set of equipment will be required.
- Prior to the activity, lead students in a general discussion about weather patterns. The following topics should be covered: What are air masses and fronts? What factors influence weather? What tools can be used to predict the weather? How does a barometer work? What is relative humidity? Have students look at cloud charts and review how clouds can indicate fair or stormy weather.

Extensions

- Students can create more extensive weather stations by designing instruments to measure wind speed, wind direction, and precipitation.

Teacher Preparation (continued)

Pre-Lab Answers

1. A barometer measures atmospheric, or baro-metric, pressure which is the pressure exerted on the surface of Earth by the atmosphere.

2. Humidity is the amount of water vapor present in the air.

3. Relative humidity is the ratio of the amount of water vapor actually in the air compared to the maximum amount that the air can contain at a specific temperature.

4. Generally, increasing atmospheric pressure indicates fair weather approaching, and decreasing atmospheric pressure indicates precipitation or stormy weather approaching.

Sample pressure, humidity, and temperature graphs are shown below.

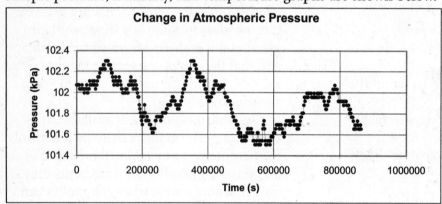

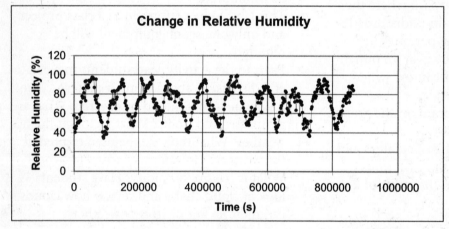

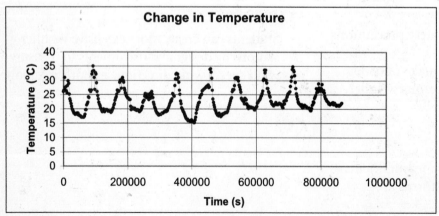

LAB 9 Probeware Activity

Predicting the Weather

What will the weather be like tomorrow? You could watch the weather forecast on television, but you probably know more about predicting the weather than you realize. If you look outside early in the morning and see high, wispy clouds in a bright blue sky, you know it will be a beautiful day. But if you see low, dark clouds and a strong wind blowing, you know a storm is on the way. In this activity you will learn more about predicting the weather and use probes to monitor atmospheric pressure, relative humidity, and temperature. You will make daily observations of clouds and weather conditions.

What You'll Investigate

- What do changes in atmospheric pressure indicate about upcoming weather conditions?
- How can you use clouds to predict clear or stormy weather?
- How is relative humidity related to temperature changes?

Goals

Create a weather station.
Measure changes in atmospheric pressure, temperature, and relative humidity.
Observe changing weather conditions.
Predict the next day's weather based on data and observations.

Materials

CBL 2 or LabPro units (2)
TI graphing calculators (2)
DataMate program
AC adapter (2)
link cables (2)
barometer
relative-humidity sensor
temperature probe
cloud chart
Beaufort wind scale

Safety Precautions

- Always wear safety goggles in the laboratory.

Pre-Lab

1. What does a barometer measure?

2. What is humidity?

3. What is relative humidity?

4. Predict what increasing and decreasing atmospheric pressure indicate about upcoming weather.

Probeware Activity 9 (continued)

Procedure

Part A: Preparing the First CBL System

1. Connect the barometer into channel 1 of the CBL 2 unit. Use a link cable to connect the CBL 2 unit to the graphing calculator as shown in **Figure 1**. Connect the AC adapter to the CBL 2 unit and plug the adapter into an outlet near the monitoring location.

Figure 1

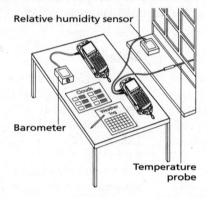

2. Turn on the calculator and start DataMate. Press [CLEAR] to reset the program. The barometer should be recognized automatically. If not, turn to page *vi* for instructions on how to set up the probe manually.

3. Select **SETUP** on the DataMate main screen to set up the time interval between data points and the length of time the data will be collected.

4. Press the up arrow once until the cursor is beside the **MODE** line. Press [ENTER].

5. Select **TIME GRAPH.** Select **CHANGE TIME SETTINGS.** The screen will display "Enter time between samples in seconds."

6. Press [7] [2] [0] [0] [ENTER]. The screen will display "Enter number of samples." Press [6] [0].

7. Select **OK.** Select **OK** again. The calculator and CBL 2 unit are ready to obtain atmospheric pressure readings every two hours for five days.

Part B: Preparing the Second CBL System

1. Connect the temperature probe into channel 1 and the relative humidity probe into channel 2 of the other CBL 2 unit. Use a link cable to connect the CBL 2 unit to the graphing calculator. Connect the AC adapter to the CBL 2 unit and plug the adapter into an outlet near the monitoring location.

2. Turn on the calculator and start DataMate. Press [CLEAR] to reset the program. The temperature and relative humidity probes should be recognized automatically. If not, turn to page *vi* for instructions on how to set up the probes manually.

3. Select **SETUP.** Press the up arrow once to select **MODE: TIMEGRAPH.** Press [ENTER].

4. Select **TIME GRAPH.** Select **CHANGE TIME SETTINGS.** The screen will display "Enter time between samples in seconds."

5. Press [7] [2] [0] [0] [ENTER]. The screen will display "Enter number of samples." Press [6] [0] [ENTER].

6. Select **OK.** Select **OK** again. The calculator and CBL 2 are now ready to collect temperature and relative humidity readings every two hours for five days.

7. Select **START** on both calculators at the same time. A screen will appear that tells you to press "enter" to continue. Press [ENTER] on each calculator at the same time. The calculators now can be disconnected and the CBL 2 units will continue to collect data.

34 Lab 9

Probeware Activity 9 (continued)

Part C: Collecting Data

1. During the five-day period, you will maintain a weather table. Prepare a chart similar to the one in the **Data Table.** Each day, record your weather observations. Use the cloud chart when recording cloud observations. Use the Beaufort wind scale when recording wind observations. Precipitation should be described by type (such as rain or snow) and amount (light, medium, or heavy).

2. After the data collection is complete, reattach the calculators. Press ⎡ ON ⎤ to turn them on.

3. On both calculators, start DataMate. A screen will appear indicating that data has been collected. Press ⎡ENTER⎤. Select **TOOLS,** and select **RETRIEVE DATA.** The calculator connected to the CBL 2 and barometer will display a pressure-time graph. Sketch and label this graph in the space provided. When you are finished, press ⎡ENTER⎤. Select **QUIT.** Follow the directions on the screen.

4. On the calculator connected to the temperature and relative-humidity probes, you are given the option to plot temperature or relative humidity. To plot both, select **MORE.** Then select **L2 and L3 vs L1.** A graph with both sets of data plotted on one axis will be displayed. Use the left/right arrow keys to trace the graph and the up/down arrow keys to select the graphs. Sketch and label this graph in the space provided.

5. When you are finished with the graph, press ⎡ENTER⎤. Select **RETURN TO GRAPH SCREEN.** Then select **MAIN SCREEN.** Select **QUIT.** Follow the directions on the screen.

Cleanup and Disposal

1. Turn off the graphing calculators and disconnect the probes and CBL 2 units.

2. Return all equipment as directed by your teacher.

Experimental Graph: Atmospheric Pressure

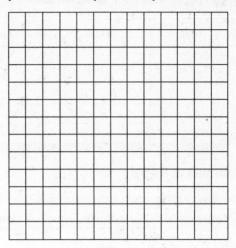

Experimental Graph: Temperature and Relative Humidity

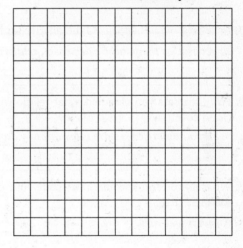

Probeware Activity 9 (continued)

Data Table: Weather Observations

Day	Time	Clouds	Precipitation	Wind
1				
2				
3				
4				
5				

Conclude and Apply

1. What did changes in air pressure indicate about the next day's weather?

   Generally, rising pressure indicates fair weather and falling pressure indicates precipitation.

2. What cloud types did you find were useful weather indicators during the measurement period?

   Answers will vary.

3. In general, what happens to the relative humidity as temperature decreases? Explain.

   In general, as temperature decreases, relative humidity increases.

4. From the data you obtained, what relationship did you notice between barometric pressure and cloud cover?

   When barometric pressure is low, cloudy days are more common.

5. What do you think would have made your model weather station more efficient for predicting weather?

   Answers will vary.

6. Use the information you obtained from the graphs and observations to predict what the weather will be like tomorrow.

   Answers will vary.

LAB 10 Teacher Preparation

How are distance and light intensity related?

Purpose

Students will observe that as the distance increases from a light source, the light intensity from that source decreases. Some students may recognize the curve as the $y = 1/x^2$ relationship. They will recognize the importance of using the terms *absolute magnitude* and *apparent magnitude* when discussing light intensity from stars. Students will learn several terms that are used in the study of light.

Time Requirements

one 45-minute class period

Advance Preparation

Prepare student lab stations with the required materials at each location. This will enable students to begin working immediately.

Safety Information

Students should observe safe laboratory procedures and wear lab aprons and goggles during the entire lab.

Teaching Tips

- Prepare the CBL 2 system for the students by linking the graphing calculator and the CBL 2 unit. Make sure the DataMate program is loaded, the light-intensity sensor is attached, and the system is ready to use.
- Students may share a single light source if multiple 60-W bulbs create too much light in the room.
- If 60-W bulbs create too much light in the room, students may use high-powered, AA-battery flashlights with the bare bulbs exposed.

- Make sure students do not set their light sources against a wall because of the chance of reflected light.

Extensions

- Have students research and find the formula for illuminance.
- Students can compare their graph to a graph of the formula to see if their data were precise.
- Students should explain their sources for experimental error.

Pre-Lab Answers

1. Yes, the farther you move away from the light the less intense it appears.

2. As the distance away from a star increases, the light intensity decreases.

3. Possible answer: The intensity of light varies as the distance from the light source changes.

4. Check students' graphs.

A graph of sample light data is shown below.

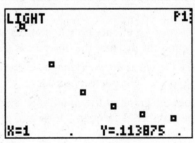

LAB
10 Probeware Activity

How are distance and light intensity related?

As you look up into the night sky, some stars seem to be brighter than others. Do these stars give off different amounts of light or is there another reason that these stars appear to vary in light intensity? In this activity you will explore the relationship between light intensity and distance. You also will investigate why scientists must classify stars according to absolute magnitude and apparent magnitude.

What You'll Investigate

- What is the relationship between light intensity and distance?

Goals

Collect light intensity and distance data.
Investigate the relationship between distance and light intensity.
Discover why stars must be classified according to apparent and absolute magnitude.

Materials

CBL 2 and LabPro unit
TI graphing calculator
Link cable
DataMate program
light-intensity sensor
lamp with 60-watt incandes-
  cent bulb
meterstick or measuring tape
masking tape
pen or marker
darkened room

Safety Precautions 🥽 🦺

- Always wear safety goggles and a lab apron during laboratory activities.

Pre-Lab

1. Does there appear to be a relationship between the intensity of a porch light or street lamp and distance?

2. Based on your experience of light sources and distance, infer the relationship between light intensity and the distance the observer is from the star.

3. Infer why the terms *apparent magnitude* and *absolute* (or actual) *magnitude* must be used when referring to the light intensity of stars.

4. What does the graph of the equation $y = 1 / x^2$ look like? If you are not sure, prepare a table using the numbers 1 through 5 for x and graph your results.

Probeware Activity 10 (continued)

Procedure

Part A: Preparing the CBL System

Figure 1

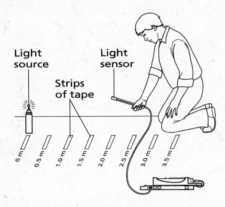

1. Set up the calculator and CBL 2 unit as shown in **Figure 1.** Plug the light intensity probe into channel 1 of the CBL 2 unit.

2. Turn on the calculator and start DataMate. Press CLEAR to reset the program. The light intensity probe should automatically be recognized. If not, turn to page *vi* for instructions on how to manually set up the probe.

3. Select **SETUP.** Press the up arrow key once to select **MODE: TIME GRAPH** and press ENTER.

4. Select **EVENTS WITH ENTRY.** Select **OK** to return to the main screen. Select **START.**

5. You should see a screen that says "PRESS [ENTER] TO COLLECT OR [STO] TO STOP." The light intensity reading will vary as you move the probe. You are ready to collect data.

Part B: Collecting Data

1. Put a strip of masking tape on the lab table or floor starting at the light source. Mark off the distances 1.0, 1.5, 2.0, 2.5, 3.0, and 3.5 meters, moving away from the light source.

2. Position the probe so that the end of the probe is lined up with the 1.0-m line. Press ENTER to record the first measurement. Key the distance measurement into the calculator. Press ENTER.

3. Repeat this procedure for each distance measurement. After you have completed all of your data collection press STO. A graph of the data should appear.

4. Use the arrow keys to scroll through the points on the graph. For each distance (x), write the corresponding light intensity (y) in the **Data Table.** Sketch and label the graph of your experimental data from your calculator screen in the space provided.

5. Press ENTER. Select **QUIT.** Follow the directions on the screen.

Cleanup and Disposal

1. Turn off the graphing calculator and disconnect the light intensity probe and CBL 2.

2. Put the used masking tape into the container designated by your teacher.

3. Return all equipment to the proper location as directed by your teacher.

Experiment Graph: Light Intensity

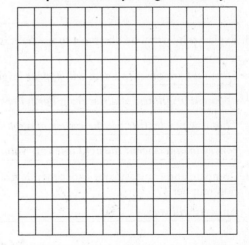

Probeware Activity 10 (continued)

Data Table

Distance (m) (x)	Light Intensity (y)
1.0	0.113875
1.5	0.07501
2.0	0.047804
2.5	0.03323
3.0	0.025457
3.5	0.020598

Conclude and Apply

1. What is the relationship between light intensity and distance from the light source?

As distance increases, light intensity decreases.

2. What are some of the sources for error in this experiment?

Possible answers: errors in measuring distance; error in placing the probe; inaccuracy of the probe; additional light sources in the room

3. Explain why it can be deceptive to use light intensity of stars to estimate their distance from Earth.

Stars that are closer to Earth will appear brighter than stars that are farther away. The apparent brightness of a star from Earth does not give a true value of its actual brightness. That is why scientists use the system of apparent magnitude and absolute magnitude to clearly convey to others what the light intensity value means.

4. Compare and contrast your experimental graph with the graph that you drew in pre-lab question number 4.

Answers will vary.

Lab 10   39

How fast do you walk?

Purpose

Students will use a motion sensor to obtain a distance-time graph as they walk away from and then toward the motion sensor. They will analyze the graph to find where their speed was fastest and slowest. Students will then calculate their average speed at various points and compare it to the average speed for the entire distance.

Time Requirements

30 minutes

Advance Preparation

- Install DataMate on the calculators.
- Prepare an unobstructed area in front of the motion sensor that is at least 2 meters long and at least 2 meters wide. The motion sensor must have the object that it is measuring in view at all times.

Safety Information

Remind students to review all safety precautions and to observe laboratory rules.

Teaching Tips

- Before beginning the activity, discuss the difference between average speed and instantaneous speed. The average speed is the total distance traveled divided by the amount of time it took to travel that distance. In this activity, students will determine their average speed and approximate instantaneous speed over a short time interval.
- Review that if speed is constant, the graph of the motion on a distance-time graph will be a straight line, and the steepness of the line

is related to the speed. If speed is not constant, the graph of the motion is not a straight line. The instantaneous speed is the steepness of the graph at a single point. An approximate value for instantaneous speed can be calculated by finding the average speed in a short time interval.

Extensions

Another graph that is available on the DataMate program is a velocity-time graph. After students have obtained their data and determined average speeds, ask them to prepare a graph of time and their average speeds. Have them choose the velocity-time graph option and compare this graph to their average speed graph.

Pre-Lab Answers

1. 1.9 m/s; 1.2 m/s

2. The steepness of the line on the graph is greater if you walk quickly.

3. Your speed was fastest at points where the line on the graph is the steepest.

4. It will be a horizontal line during that time because your distance from the detector didn't change.

A sample distance-time graph is shown below.

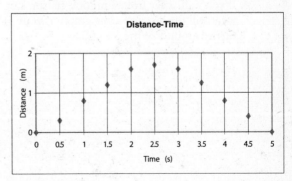

LAB 11 · Probeware Activity

How fast do you walk?

Whether you walk fast or slow, your speed is almost always changing. When you walk from your classroom to the lunchroom, you may start out walking quickly. If the hall becomes crowded with other students, you probably will slow down. You can describe how fast you walked to the lunchroom by using your average speed for the entire trip or by your instantaneous speed at each point along the way. In this activity, you will use a motion sensor to record your speed as you walk. By analyzing your graph, you can compare your instantaneous speed and average speed.

What You'll Investigate

- How does your instantaneous speed change as you walk?
- How can you use a distance-time graph to determine when your speed is fastest and when it is slowest?

Goals

Measure your change in distance as you walk.
Analyze a distance-time graph.
Estimate instantaneous speed.
Calculate average speed.

Materials

CBL 2 or LabPro unit
TI graphing calculator
link cable
DataMate program
motion sensor
meterstick
masking tape

Safety Precautions

- Always wear safety goggles.

Pre-Lab

1. Suppose you walk in a straight line away from a table for a distance of 8 meters in 4.3 seconds. You then turn around and walk 8 meters toward the table in 6.8 seconds. What is your average speed as you walk away from the table? Toward the table?
2. Compare the steepness of a line on a distance-time graph when you walk quickly and when you walk slowly.
3. How can you determine where your speed is greatest by looking at a distance-time graph of motion?
4. If you walk away from a motion sensor, stop, turn around, and walk back toward the sensor, what will the distance-time graph of your motion look like for the time you stopped and turned around? Why?

Probeware Activity 11 (continued)

Procedure

Part A: Preparing the CBL System

1. Place the motion sensor on the edge of a surface about 1 meter above the floor. Flip up the top of the sensor so that it points along a horizontal, clear space about 2-m long. The motion sensor must have the object that it is measuring in view at all times.

2. Use a meterstick to measure a straight, 2-m path away from the motion sensor. Use masking tape to mark the start and stop lines.

3. Plug the motion sensor connector cable into the DIG/SONIC port on the right side of the CBL 2 unit, as shown in **Figure 1.** Use a link cable to connect the CBL 2 unit to the graphing calculator.

4. Start the DataMate program. Press (CLEAR) to reset the program.

Figure 1

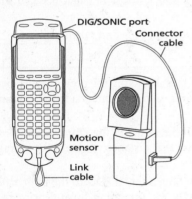

Part B: Collecting Data

1. Stand with your back at least 45 cm from the motion sensor. Have a partner select **START** on the calculator. When you hear the CBL 2 unit make a tone, begin walking along the path away from the motion sensor. Walk to the 2-m mark, turn around, and walk back. The entire trip should last 5 seconds.

2. When the measurement is complete, the calculator will display a screen giving you a choice of graphs. Press (ENTER) to choose **DIG-DISTANCE,** the distance-time graph.

3. A graph of your motion will appear on the screen. Use the left and right arrow keys to move the cursor along the curve. Data for time (x) and distance (y) will appear at the bottom of the screen. Find the selected time values listed in the **Data Table** on the x-axis of the curve and write the corresponding distance values in the **Data Table.** Round the distance values to the nearest tenth of a meter.

4. Sketch and label the graph on your calculator screen in the space below.

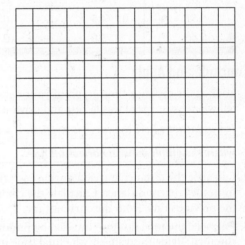

5. When you are finished with the graph, press (ENTER). Select **QUIT.** Follow the directions on the calculator screen.

Cleanup and Disposal

1. Turn off the calculator. Disconnect the motion sensor and CBL 2 unit.

2. Return all equipment to the proper location as directed by your teacher. Answer the questions on the following page.

Probeware Activity 11 (continued)

Data Table: Selected Data Points

Distance from Detector (m)	Elapsed Time (s)	Distance Traveled	Change in Time	Instantaneous Speed (m/s)
0.54	0.0	–	–	–
0.98	0.5	0.44	0.5	0.9
1.27	1.0	0.29	0.5	0.6
2.10	1.5	0.83	0.5	1.7
1.99	2.0	0.11	0.5	0.2
1.85	2.5	0.14	0.5	0.3
1.62	3.0	0.23	0.5	0.5
1.20	3.5	0.42	0.5	0.8
0.83	4.0	0.37	0.5	0.7
0.51	4.5	0.32	0.5	0.6
0.40	5.0	0.11	0.5	0.2

Conclude and Apply

1. Look at the distance-time graph of your data. Without looking at the data table, how can you tell where your speed was fastest and slowest?

   It was fastest where the curve is steepest. It was slowest when stopping and turning around,

   where the graph shows a horizontal line.

2. Calculate the distance traveled during each time interval by subtracting the previous distance from the current distance. Calculate the change in time over each time interval by subtracting the previous time from the current time.

3. Calculate the total distance traveled by finding the sum of the values in the *Distance Traveled* column. Divide this value by the total time it took to travel that distance to obtain the average speed.

4. Calculate the approximate instantaneous speed over each time interval. Record the information in the **Data Table.** Round your answers to the nearest tenth. You can obtain an approximate value for your instantaneous speed at each time interval by using this formula:

   $$instantaneous\ speed = \frac{distance\ traveled}{change\ in\ time}$$

5. Compare your average speed to your approximate instantaneous speed. Is it possible for average speed to be greater than instantaneous speed? Explain.

   Yes. You can move more slowly for a short period of time. Your instantaneous speed in this time

   period would be less than your average speed.

6. Notice that the instantaneous speed varied as you walked. What would your graph have looked like if you had traveled the entire time at the same instantaneous speed?

   It would look like an upside down V.

LAB 12 Teacher Preparation

Transforming Energy

Purpose

Students will observe the transformation of kinetic energy to thermal energy by vigorously shaking a container of sand. Students will use the CBL 2 unit and a temperature probe to collect data.

Time Requirements

one 45-minute class period

Advance Preparation

- Install DataMate on the calculators.
- Set up the CBL 2 and temperature probes prior to class to allow additional time for multiple trials or to allow students to do a lab extension.
- Bring the sand into your classroom the day before the lab day so it will be at room temperature.

Safety Information

Remind students to hold the jar with two hands. Extinguish all flames before beginning this activity.

Teaching Tips

- Before the lab, briefly discuss the concept of energy and ask students to give examples. Students should be able to describe kinetic, potential, chemical, radiant, and thermal energy.
- Have students think of ways that energy changes form. For example, a lightbulb changes electrical energy to radiant and thermal energy.
- Ask students to define friction. Explain that friction transforms kinetic energy to thermal

energy. Have them demonstrate this by rubbing their hands together, first slowly and then quickly. They will notice that the faster they move their hands, the warmer their hands feel.
- Members of each lab group may take turns shaking the jar. Some members may become tired and not shake the jar consistently during the entire shaking period.

Extensions

- Students can modify the lab to test the shaking of different materials and observe how the temperature changes compare. Materials such as dirt, small gravel (aquarium gravel), flour, sugar, or water may be used in place of sand. Extinguish all flames in the lab before testing powders such as flour.
- Students could also do a comparison: shake, rattle, and roll the same material to investigate which method transfers more energy.

Pre-Lab Answers

1. Kinetic energy is the energy an object has due to its motion.

2. As you rub your hands together, friction between their surfaces converts the kinetic energy of your moving hands into thermal energy, making your hands feel warmer.

3. Answers will vary. Students may hypothesize that the temperature of the sand will increase as friction transforms kinetic energy from the moving sand into thermal energy.

4. It is important to wear gloves so that your hands do not transfer thermal energy to the jar.

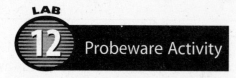

LAB 12 Probeware Activity

Transforming Energy

Everything you do involves a change of energy from one form to another. When you bounce a basketball, potential energy changes to kinetic energy to keep the ball bouncing. Electrical energy is transformed into radiant energy when you flip a light switch.

Friction is a force that converts kinetic energy to thermal energy when two objects rub against one another. Friction converts some of the kinetic energy of a moving match into thermal energy. This thermal energy causes the temperature of the match head to increase until chemicals in the match head catch fire. Friction also changes kinetic energy to thermal energy when the space shuttle returns to Earth. As the shuttle speeds back through the atmosphere, air molecules rush against it. Friction converts kinetic energy from the shuttle into thermal energy. The underside of the shuttle becomes so hot that it must be covered with special heat-resistant tiles to keep from burning up.

In this activity, you will use a temperature probe to look for evidence that friction causes an energy transformation when you shake sand in a jar.

What You'll Investigate

- How can friction cause an energy transformation to occur when you shake a jar of sand?
- What evidence suggests that an energy change has occurred?

Goals

Collect data on energy transformations.
Measure temperature of a solid.
Compare the temperature before and after shaking a solid.
Calculate any temperature changes that occur.

Materials

CBL 2 or LabPro unit
TI graphing calculator
link cable
DataMate program
temperature probe
hot mitt or gloves (2)
sand (250 mL)
clean, plastic jar (approx. 1,000 mL with screw lid)
timer

Safety Precautions 🥽 🧤 🚯

- Always wear safety goggles and a lab apron.
- Wash your hands before leaving the lab area.
- Extinguish all flames before beginning this activity.

Pre-Lab

1. What is kinetic energy?

2. Describe how friction produces an energy transformation that makes your hands feel warm when you rub them together rapidly.

3. Hypothesize what energy transformation will occur when you shake sand in a jar. How is friction between the sand particles related to this?

4. Why is it important to wear gloves while holding the jar during shaking and temperature readings?

Lab 12   45

Probeware Activity 12 (continued)

Procedure

Part A: Preparing the CBL System

1. Set up the calculator and CBL 2 unit, as shown in **Figure 1.** Plug the temperature probe into channel 1 of the CBL 2 unit.

2. Turn on the calculator and start DataMate. Press CLEAR to reset the program. The temperature probe should be recognized automatically. If not, turn to page *vi* for instructions on how to set up the probe manually.

Figure 1

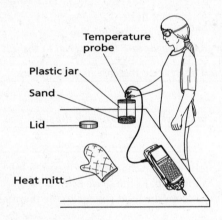

Temperature probe
Plastic jar
Sand
Lid
Heat mitt

Part B: Collecting Data

1. Fill the plastic jar about $\frac{1}{4}$ full of sand.

2. The calculator screen should display the room air temperature measured by the probe in the upper right corner of the screen. Record the room air temperature, to one decimal place, in the **Data Table.**

3. Place the temperature probe into the sand, as shown in **Figure 1** and allow it to sit undisturbed for about one minute. Record the temperature, to one decimal place, in the **Data Table,** as the start temperature.

4. For the next six minutes you will alternate shaking the closed jar of sand for one minute and then measuring the sand temperature during the next minute. Tighten the lid securely on the jar. Put on a pair of gloves and pick up the jar. Always hold the jar with two gloved hands. Shake the jar vigorously (hard) for one minute.

5. Remove the jar's lid and place the temperature probe into the sand. After about 30 to 45 seconds, record the sand's temperature in the **Data Table.** Tighten the lid back on the jar and repeat the procedure three times. Record the temperature for each trial in the **Data Table.**

6. Select **QUIT.** Follow the directions on the calculator screen.

Cleanup and Disposal

1. Turn off the graphing calculator and disconnect the temperature probe and the CBL 2 unit.

2. Clean off the temperature probe with a paper towel.

3. Return the CBL 2 and other laboratory equipment to its proper place as directed by your teacher.

Probeware Activity 12 (continued)

Data Table: Sand Temperature

Time (minutes)	Task	Temperature °C
Start	Measure temperature	24.3
0 – 1	Shake jar	
1 – 2	Measure temperature	25.1
2 – 3	Shake jar	
3 – 4	Measure temperature	25.6
4 – 5	Shake jar	
5 – 6 (End)	Measure temperature	25.9

Conclude and Apply

1. Compare the sand temperature readings. Describe any change.

Student answers will vary depending on how hard they shake the jar and the material in the jar.

The sample data shows an increase of 2.6 °C. They should observe an increase in temperature.

2. Suggest a possible explanation for your observations.

Friction transformed kinetic energy of the sand into thermal energy, which heated the sand.

3. As you shook the jar of sand, chemical energy from the food you ate changed to kinetic energy in your muscles. This, in turn, provided kinetic energy to the sand. In the space below, create a concept map showing the series of energy transformations from the food you ate to the thermal energy released to the air.

chemical energy → kinetic energy → kinetic energy → thermal energy → thermal energy
(food)　　　(muscles)　　　(sand)　　　(sand)　　　(air)

4. How do you think your results would change if you shook the sand faster? How would the results change if you shook the sand longer? Explain.

Shaking the sand faster would cause the sand to warm more quickly. Shaking the sand longer

would increase the amount of kinetic energy converted to thermal energy, increasing the final

temperature.

5. A meteor is a meteoroid that falls through Earth's atmosphere. Based on the results you obtained in this experiment, explain why a meteor appears as a streak of light in the night sky.

Friction between the meteor and molecules in air transforms kinetic energy from the meteor to

thermal energy. The meteor burns up because of the tremendous increase in temperature.

We see the burning meteor as a streak of light.

Lab 12   47

LAB 13 Teacher Preparation

Endothermic and Exothermic Processes

Purpose

Students will measure temperature changes that occur as chemical compounds dissolve in water. They will collect temperature data for three minutes using the CBL 2 unit and a temperature probe. Students will use graphing calculators to observe exothermic and endothermic processes in progress and analyze data.

Time Requirements

one 45-minute class period

Advance Preparation

- Install the DataMate program on the graphing calculators.
- Prepare sets of materials or lab stations in advance to help insure that students easily complete the lab.
- Allow about 2 L of distilled water to sit overnight at room temperature.

Safety Information

Review all safety precautions. Remind students to observe all laboratory rules.

Teaching Tips

- Potassium chloride absorbs heat from its surroundings when it dissolves in water. Therefore, dissolution of potassium chloride is an endothermic process. The dissolution of calcium chloride is an exothermic process.
- Review with students the difference between chemical processes and physical processes. In this lab, they will be investigating the dissolving of a solid in water. This is a physical process.
- To help them understand why dissolution is a physical process, remind them that when they dissolve salt in water, they can still taste the salt. If the water were to evaporate, the salt would remain. It is not changed chemically.

- Lumps or chunks work better than fine-granulated material because they take longer to dissolve. Granulated material works, but it dissolves in approximately 15–25 seconds when the water in the beaker is stirred.
- Ammonium nitrate (NH_4NO_3) may be used instead of potassium chloride to demonstrate an endothermic process. It will release a larger amount of energy per gram than KCl will. If ammonium nitrate is used instead of potassium chloride, a mild ammonia odor may occur when it is mixed with water. Caution students not to intentionally inhale the fumes near the beaker. Small first aid cold packs often use ammonium nitrate and water.
- Sodium chloride also can be substituted for potassium chloride, however it produces a smaller temperature change.
- The solution may become saturated and additional material will not dissolve. If students see undissolved solids in the bottom of the beaker, the solution is probably saturated.

Extensions

- Have students hypothesize what will happen if they try increasing the amount of solid or decreasing the amount of water. Allow students to perform the experiment to test their hypotheses.
- Have students research to find out how calcium chloride is used when outdoor temperatures drop below freezing.
- Have students make a list of everyday activities that use endothermic and exothermic processes. The class can compile all of their items and make a master list.
- Have students research to find out about cold packs. Students can find the different types of chemicals used, methods of packaging, and shelf life of these products.

Teacher Preparation (continued)

- Exothermic processes are common and the class can generate a long list of activities that use them. Students can pick a process to research and present their report to the class. Some students may be interested in researching how pyrotechnics are used for stunts in the movies.

Pre-Lab Answers

1. A physical change is one in which the form or appearance of a substance changes but its composition stays the same.

2. Possible examples of physical change are changing shape, changing state, and dissolving.

3. An exothermic process is one that releases heat.

4. An endothermic process is one that absorbs heat.

Sample graphs of both endothermic and exothermic processes are shown below.

Dissolving of KCL in water

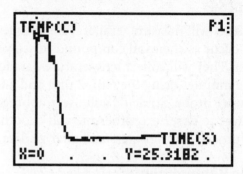

Dissolving of CaCl$_2$ in water

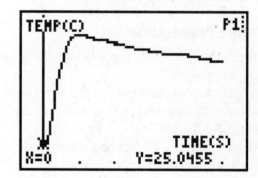

LAB 13 Probeware Activity

Endothermic and Exothermic Processes

When a substance dissolves in water, a change in energy usually occurs. Although a change in energy can be a sign of a chemical change, the dissolving of a substance is a physical change. The water molecules break apart into positive and negative parts and surround the particles of the substance that is dissolving. In some cases, dissolving releases heat energy into the surroundings. Processes that release heat energy are called *exothermic*. In other cases, dissolving absorbs heat energy from the surroundings. Processes that absorb heat are called *endothermic*. How can you tell if heat energy is released or absorbed? In this activity you will collect data and search for clues to determine which type of heat energy transfer is taking place.

What You'll Investigate

- What happens when $CaCl_2$ and KCl are added to water?
- Will these processes produce temperature changes?

Goals

Measure the change in temperature when substances are added to water.

Calculate any change in water temperature that occurs during the process.

Graph temperature changes over time.

Materials

CBL 2 or LabPro unit
TI graphing calculator
link cable
DataMate program
temperature probe
400-mL beaker
100-mL beaker
plastic spoon
glass stirring rod
distilled water
    (room temperature)
5.0g calcium chloride ($CaCl_2$)
5.0g potassium chloride (KCl)

Safety Precautions

- Always wear safety goggles and a lab apron.
- Report any spills to your teacher.
- Do not taste, eat, or drink any materials used in the lab.
- Wash your hands before leaving the laboratory.

Pre-Lab

1. What is a physical change?

2. What are examples of physical change?

3. What is an exothermic process?

4. What is an endothermic process?

Lab 13   49

Probeware Activity 13 (continued)

Procedure

Part A: Preparing the CBL System

1. Set up the calculator and CBL 2 unit, as shown in **Figure 1.** Plug the temperature probe into channel 1 of the CBL 2 unit.

2. Turn on the calculator and start DataMate. Press CLEAR to reset the program. The temperature probe should be recognized automatically. If not, turn to page *vi* for instructions on how to set up the probe manually.

Figure 1

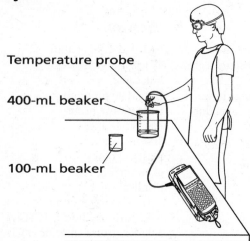

Temperature probe

400-mL beaker

100-mL beaker

Part B: Collecting Data

1. Add 100 mL of room-temperature water to the 400-mL beaker.

2. Place the temperature probe in the water.

3. Use a balance to measure 5.0 g of potassium chloride on a piece of weighing paper or in a weighing dish.

4. On the graphing calculator, select **START** to begin the data collection. About five seconds after data collection has begun, carefully add the potassium chloride to the water. Make sure all of the potassium chloride is emptied into the water. Data will be collected for 180 seconds.

5. Using a glass stirring rod, gently stir the water in the beaker for about 20 seconds to help the potassium chloride dissolve.

6. After 180 seconds have lapsed, the calculator will display a graph of temperature versus time with temperature on the *y*-axis and time on the *x*-axis. Sketch and label this graph in your **Science Journal.**

Part C: Examining the Data

1. Return to the main screen by pressing ENTER.

2. Select **ANALYZE.**

3. Select **STATISTICS.**

4. Press ENTER to select the beginning of the temperature graph. Use the right arrow key to select the last temperature data point reached. Press ENTER to select this point.

5. Your calculator will display the minimum and maximum temperatures reached. Determine which of these is the starting temperature and which is the ending temperature—the temperature after all of the solid dissolved. Record these temperatures in the **Data Table.** When you are finished, press ENTER. Select **RETURN TO MAIN SCREEN.**

6. Rinse your beaker thoroughly and repeat parts **B** and **C** using 5 g of calcium chloride.

7. When you are finished, press ENTER. Select **RETURN TO MAIN SCREEN.** Select **QUIT.** Follow the directions on the screen.

Cleanup and Disposal

1. Turn off the graphing calculator and disconnect the temperature probe and CBL 2 unit.

2. Clean and return all equipment as directed by your teacher and answer the questions on the following page.

50   Lab 13

Probeware Activity 13 (continued)

Data Table: Dissolving of KCl and CaCl₂

Substance	Starting Temperature (°C)	Ending Temperature (°C)	Temperature Change (°C)	Type of Process
Potassium chloride (KCl)	25.31	19.61	–5.70	*Endothermic*
Calcium chloride (CaCl₂)	25.04	30.16	+5.12	*Exothermic*

Conclude and Apply

1. Calculate the temperature change for each substance by subtracting the starting temperature from the ending temperature. Record your results in the **Data Table.** How are these temperature changes different?

   Student results may vary. The potassium chloride solution should be cooler (negative change)

   and the calcium chloride solution should be warmer (positive change) than the starting

   temperature of the water.

2. Which process is endothermic and which is exothermic?

   Potassium chloride dissolving in water is an endothermic process while calcium chloride

   dissolving in water is an exothermic process.

3. Look at your graphs. Suggest a possible explanation for why the temperature of the water changed rapidly at first and then leveled off.

   Student answers will vary. The temperature of the water changed rapidly when the

   solid was dissolving. The temperature of the water leveled off when the solid was

   completely dissolved.

4. From your results, infer what the result might be if twice as much potassium chloride was added to the same amount of water.

   The water will cool more, possibly cooling twice as much. Students could test this as an

   extension. Teacher Note: When the water becomes saturated with the substance being dissolved

   no additional cooling will be observed.

Lab 13   **51**

LAB 14 Teacher Preparation

Thermal Conductivity

Purpose

Students will compare the thermal conductivity of different types of materials. Each material will be partially submerged in hot water and a temperature probe will record the change in temperature of the portion of the material that is not submerged. Each student group will test a different material. The results from all of the groups will be combined and the students will compare the temperature changes of the different materials.

Time Requirements

one 45-minute class period

Materials

Students should test the thermal conductivity of several different materials. Some possible materials include steel, aluminum, copper, tin, zinc, plastic, and wood. Items must be long enough to be partially submerged in water and able to have a probe attached to the top of the item that does not touch the water.

Advance Preparation

• Prepare lab stations in advance so students can begin promptly.
• Allow each of the materials tested to equilibrate at room temperature before beginning.
• Prepare about 1L of hot water prior to the beginning of class. A temperature of about 40°C should be sufficient. A hot plate can be used to keep the water warm.
• Prepare an overhead transparency or a space on the chalkboard for students to write their lab data.

Teaching Tips

• Make sure there is good thermal contact between the probe and the material.

• Discuss the difference between heat and temperature. Heat is the transfer of thermal energy between two objects having different temperatures. Temperature is the average kinetic energy of the particles in a substance.
• Have the students predict whether the item will be a thermal conductor or an insulator. Have them compare their predictions to their results.

Extensions

Have students research to find out what properties make some materials good thermal conductors and others thermal insulators.

Pre-Lab Answers

1. Heat is transferred faster in a thermal conductor than in a thermal insulator.

2. Students might predict that metals are good thermal conductors. They might predict that plastic and foam cups are insulators.

3. The top of the material would get warmer more quickly than if it were an insulator.

4. Heat flows from a warmer object to a colder object.

A sample graph showing the temperature increase of copper and plastic is shown below.

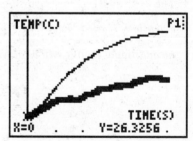

Probe 1-copper (top)
Probe 2-plastic (bottom)

LAB
14   Probeware Activity

Thermal Conductivity

Heat is thermal energy that flows from a warmer material to a cooler material. One way that thermal energy is transferred is by a process called conduction. Conduction occurs because the particles in a warmer material are moving faster than the particles in a cooler material. When these materials are in contact, the particles collide with one another and some of the kinetic energy of the faster-moving particles is transferred to the slower-moving particles. When the warm material looses some kinetic energy, its temperature drops. When the cool material gains kinetic energy, its temperature rises. A material that is a thermal conductor transfers thermal energy more rapidly than a material that is a thermal insulator. In this lab you will observe and compare the thermal conduction of several different materials.

What You'll Investigate

- How do materials vary in thermal conductivity?
- Do similar materials have similar thermal conductivity?

Goals

Collect temperature data.
Compare the thermal conductivity of various materials.
Analyze temperature data and look for trends in various materials.

Materials

CBL 2 or LabPro unit
TI graphing calculator
temperature probe
link cable
DataMate program
hot mitt or thermal glove
test strips of various materials
400-mL beaker
masking tape
hot plate
tap water

Safety Precautions

- Always wear safety goggles and a lab apron.
- Observe laboratory rules.
- Use care near heat sources and when handling hot objects.

Pre-Lab

1. What is the difference between a thermal conductor and a thermal insulator?

2. Form a hypothesis about what types of materials are conductors. What types of materials do you think are insulators?

3. If the bottom half of a long strip of material is placed in hot water, how would you determine if it was a thermal conductor or insulator?

4. Describe the direction of heat flow between two objects.

Probeware Activity 14 (continued)

Procedure

Part A: Preparing the CBL System

1. Set up the calculator and CBL 2 unit, as shown in **Figure 1**. Plug the temperature probe into channel 1 of the CBL 2 unit.

2. Turn on the calculator and start DataMate. Press [CLEAR] to reset the program. The temperature probe should be recognized automatically. If not, turn to page *vi* for instructions on how to set up the probe manually.

Figure 1

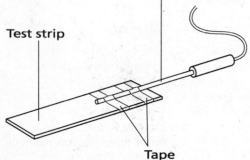

Part B: Collecting Data

1. Put on your lab apron and safety goggles.

2. Lay the temperature probe over the metal strip so the bottom of the probe is 7 cm from the end, as shown in **Figure 1**. Tape the probe to the metal strip.

3. Fill the 400-mL beaker to the 150–mL mark with hot water obtained from your teacher.

4. Select **START** on your calculator to begin data collection. Using a gloved hand, place your test strip into the beaker of hot water being careful not to splash water onto the probes. The probe should not touch the hot water and should sit above the water line.

5. Data will be collected for 180 seconds. When the calculator stops, it will display a time-temperature graph with temperature on the *y*-axis and time on the *x*-axis. Sketch and label this graph in your **Science Journal.**

Part C: Examining Data

1. Return to the main screen by pressing [ENTER].

2. Select **ANALYZE.**

3. Select **STATISTICS.**

4. Press [ENTER] to select the beginning of the temperature graph. Use the right arrow key to select the end of the temperature graph. Press [ENTER].

5. Record the maximum and minimum temperatures in the **Data Table.**

6. Write your data in the group table provided by your teacher for data sharing. Fill in the remaining lines on the **Data Table** using the data from the group table.

7. When you are finished, press [ENTER]. Select **RETURN TO MAIN SCREEN.**

8. If time permits, test another sample. If not, select **QUIT.** Follow the directions on the screen.

Cleanup and Disposal

1. Turn off the graphing calculator and disconnect the temperature probes and CBL 2 unit.

2. Return all equipment as directed by your teacher.

Probeware Activity 14 (continued)

Data Table: Temperature Change of Different Materials

Type of Test Material	Minimum Temperature (°C)	Maximum Temperature (°C)	Change in Temperature (°C)
Copper	26.25	33.45	7.20
Plastic	26.33	28.61	2.28

Conclude and Apply

1. Find the change in temperature for each material tested by subtracting the minimum temperature from the maximum temperature. Record the difference in the **Data Table.** *Student answers will vary. For the sample data, the change in temperature for copper was 7.20 °C and plastic was 2.28 °C.*

2. What are some similarities of materials that are thermal insulators? What are some similarities of materials that are thermal conductors?

   Student answers may vary, although they should indicate plastic and wood materials tend to

   be thermal insulators and metals tend to be thermal conductors.

3. On a temperature-time graph, the steeper the slope of the line is, the faster the temperature change is in a given amount of time. The graph of which material had the steepest slope and, therefore, the fastest change of temperature?

   The copper test strip had the fastest change in temperature.

4. Find a student group that tested the same material that you tested. How do your temperature changes compare? If the temperature changes were not the same, what are possible reasons that they were different?

   If the items were identical in shape and size, the temperature differences are probably very small.

   However, a larger item would probably show a smaller temperature difference than a smaller

   item of the same material. Also, the temperature of the larger item would increase more slowly

   than the temperature of the smaller item.

Lab 14   55

LAB
15 Teacher Preparation

Let the Races Begin!

Purpose

Students will observe that increasing the height of a hill will increase the acceleration of a toy car that is rolling down it. Students will relate this to an increase in potential energy. Data will be collected using a motion sensor attached to a CBL 2 unit and a graphing calculator.

Time Requirements

one 45-minute class period

Advance Preparation

Prepare student lab stations with the required materials at each location. This will enable students to begin working immediately.

Materials

- A lab cart can be used in place of the toy car. It will have less friction in its axles than a toy car. The friction in the axles and the roughness of the board are primary sources of experimental error in this lab.
- Using a smooth board and a quality lab cart will improve the results for this lab.
- Other items such as wood blocks or bricks can be used instead of textbooks to elevate the ramp.
- Check with the physics department of your school to see if you can borrow any of the lab supplies that you do not have.

Safety Information

Students should observe safe laboratory procedures and wear goggles during the entire lab.

Teaching Tips

- Prepare the CBL 2 system for the students by linking the graphing calculator, the CBL 2 unit, and the motion sensor before the lab begins. Make sure the DataMate program is loaded and the system is ready to use.
- The motion sensor must be 45 cm from the car at the beginning of the run. The range of the motion sensor is 0.45 to 6.0 meters.
- Make sure students understand the difference between speed and velocity. In this experiment the motion of the toy car is in a single direction along the inclined board, so speed and velocity are the same.
- Have students discuss how potential energy is converted into kinetic energy as an object falls or moves from a higher elevation to a lower elevation.

Extensions

- Have the students find out how the speed and acceleration of a roller coaster car is related to the height of a hill.
- Advanced students may calculate the slope of the distance-time graph to find the average speed of the car. They can calculate the slope of the line for the velocity-time graph to find the average acceleration of the car.

Teacher Preparation (continued)

Pre-Lab Answers

1. Speed $= \dfrac{\text{distance}}{\text{time}}$;

   Acceleration $= \dfrac{(\text{final speed} - \text{initial speed})}{\text{time}}$

2. The kinetic energy increases and the potential energy decreases. The potential energy of the object is transformed into kinetic energy as the object falls.

3. Possible answers: The car should be placed in the middle of the board to keep it in line of sight of the motion sensor; The car must be able to roll in a straight line or it will roll off of the ramp; The car cannot be too small or the motion sensor will not detect it.

4. friction from air resistance, friction between the moving parts in the axles, and friction between the wheels and the board

A sample distance-time graph is shown below.

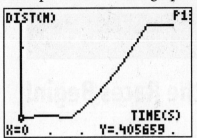

A sample acceleration-time graph is shown below.

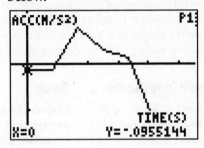

A sample velocity-time graph is shown below.

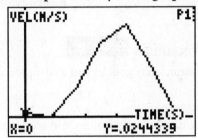

LAB 15 Probeware Activity

Let the Races Begin!

Sledding down a hill in the snow, coasting down a hill on your bike, or speeding down a hill in a roller coaster would not be the same without a steep hill. You know that the higher the hill, the faster you'll be going when you reach the bottom. This is because objects at the top of a hill have potential energy. The amount of potential energy that an object has depends upon its height above Earth. This potential energy is converted into kinetic energy—energy of motion, when the object falls downward. Whether the hill is steep or has a gentle slope, your speed at the bottom depends on the height of the hill. In this experiment you will collect distance, velocity, and acceleration data by rolling a toy car down a board at two different heights.

What You'll Investigate

- How does the height of a ramp affect speed and acceleration?

Goals

Collect distance, velocity, and acceleration data.
Compare the graphs for each trial.
Identify sources of experimental error.

Materials

CBL 2 or LabPro unit
TI graphing calculator
link cable
DataMate program
motion sensor
board (at least 1.5 m long)
toy car or lab cart

Safety Precautions

- Always wear safety goggles and a lab apron during a laboratory activity.

Pre-Lab

1. How are distance, speed, time, and acceleration related?

2. How does the kinetic and potential energy of an object change as the object falls?

3. The motion sensor works in a way that is similar to the way a radar-speed detector works. In looking at the motion sensor, the toy car, and the board, what things must be taken into consideration before starting your investigation?

4. Where are the sources of friction in this lab?

Probeware Activity 15 (continued)

Procedure

Part A: Preparing the CBL System

Figure 1

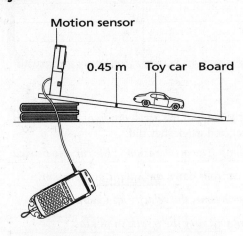

Motion sensor

0.45 m   Toy car   Board

1. Set up the calculator and CBL 2 unit, as shown in **Figure 1**. The motion sensor should be plugged into the DIG/SONIC channel that is located on the right-hand side of the CBL 2 unit.

2. Turn on the calculator and start DataMate. Press CLEAR to reset the program.

Part B: Collecting Data

1. Use textbooks to elevate the board, as shown in **Figure 1**. Put just enough textbooks under the board so that the car rolls down the ramp.

2. Position the motion sensor at the top of the ramp so that it can "see" the car as it travels down the ramp. The car must be placed at least 45 cm from the motion sensor for the sensor to operate properly. When the car and motion sensor are in place, you will hear a series of soft clicks from the motion detector.

3. Select **START** on the calculator and release the car.

Part C: Examining the Data

1. After the run is complete, the screen will display a choice of three graphs: DIG-DISTANCE, DIG-VELOCITY, AND DIG-ACCELERATION. Select **DIG-VELOCITY** to display a velocity-time graph.

2. Sketch and label this graph in your **Science Journal**.

3. Use the arrow keys to obtain the maximum *y*-value (velocity) and the *x*-value (time) that maximum velocity occurred. Write these data in the **Data Table**. Press ENTER.

4. Select **DIG-ACCELERATION** to display an acceleration-time graph.

5. Sketch and label this graph in your **Science Journal**.

6. Use the arrow keys to obtain the maximum acceleration and the time that the maximum acceleration occurred. Write these data in the **Data Table**. Press ENTER.

7. Select **DIG-DISTANCE** to display a distance-time graph.

8. Sketch and label this graph in your **Science Journal**.

9. Press ENTER. Select **MAIN SCREEN**.

10. Repeat part B and part C, Steps 1–9, using additional textbooks to elevate the ramp at a steeper angle. Record the data for each trial in the **Data Table**. Sketch and label each graph.

11. From the main screen, select **QUIT**. Follow the directions on the screen.

Cleanup and Disposal

1. Turn off the graphing calculator and disconnect the motion sensor and CBL 2 unit.

2. Return all equipment to the proper location as directed by your teacher and answer the following questions.

Probeware Activity 15 (continued)

Data Table: Run Data

	First Run	Second Run
Maximum velocity		
Time maximum velocity occurred		
Maximum acceleration		
Time maximum acceleration occurred		

Conclude and Apply

1. When did the velocity of the car reach a maximum? When did the acceleration of the car reach a maximum? Explain possible reasons why these occurred when they did.

   The velocity of the car peaked at the bottom of the ramp. The acceleration of the car also peaked

   at the bottom of the ramp, for every second that the car rolls down the hill the acceleration

   should increase. Because the acceleration increases with time, the velocity also increases with

   time. Friction in the axles and roughness in the board will vary the results in this lab.

2. Using your graphs, determine when the car appears to have completed the run or moved out of sight of the motion sensor.

   The line on the distance-time graph will be a flat line. At this point in time, the motion

   sensor no longer has the car in its line of sight.

3. If friction were not present, what would the graphs for velocity and acceleration look like?

   The slope of the graphs would be positive. The velocity of the car would continue to increase

   as it travels the length of the board.

4. Identify possible sources of experimental error in your experiment.

   Possible answers: Friction in the axles of the car; inaccuracy of the probe; a rough surface on

   the board.

5. How did increasing the height of the car's starting position affect the potential energy of the car?

   The amount of potential energy the car has depends on its height above the ground.

6. Explain why increasing the height of the car's starting position increased the car's speed at the bottom of the board.

   Increasing the height of the board increased the car's potential energy. More potential energy

   was converted to kinetic energy.

Appendix A

Using the TI-73 Graphing Calculator to Create a Histogram

A histogram is a graph that shows data divided into equal ranges and the number of data points that fall into each range. The following instructions explain how to make a histogram for the heart rate data in *Exercise and Heart Rate*.

1. **Resetting Calculator Memory** Turn on your graphing calculator and press ⌜2nd⌝ [**MEM**]. Select **Clr All Lists.** Press ⌜ENTER⌝.

2. **Creating and Entering Data Into Lists** Press ⌜LIST⌝ to access an empty data table. Name your lists before entering data. Scroll up to the title bar (the "top shelf") and over to the first empty list beyond L6 (lists L1–L6 cannot be renamed). Press ⌜2nd⌝ [**TEXT**]. Scroll to the desired letters, pressing ⌜ENTER⌝ after each. Choose a title of 5 or fewer letters. Then scroll down to **DONE.** Press ⌜ENTER⌝ twice to title your new list. Repeat for the other two variables. Enter your class data in all three lists.

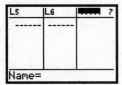  

3. **Setting up Graphs** Press ⌜2nd⌝ [**PLOT**]. Select **Plot 1** by pressing ⌜ENTER⌝. Use the arrow keys and ⌜ENTER⌝ to turn the plot on and to select the sixth graph icon, a histogram. For the Xlist, press ⌜2nd⌝ ⌜LIST⌝ and scroll down to find the resting heart rate list. Press ⌜ENTER⌝ twice. Ignore Freq.

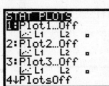 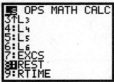 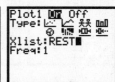

4. Repeat **Step 3** to set up Plot 2 and Plot 3, but do not turn them ON yet. The Xlists will be your exercise heart rate and recovery time lists.

5. **Plotting Data** Press ⌜ZOOM⌝. Then select **ZoomStat** to see your first histogram for resting heart rate. Use the ⌜TRACE⌝ and arrow keys to find the heart rate range that occurred in the class most often and the number of students that were in this range.

6. Press ⌜2nd⌝ [**PLOT**] to turn off Plot 1, and turn on Plot 2. Repeat step 5 for Plot 3 to see the class histogram for exercise heart rate and recovery time.

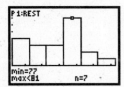 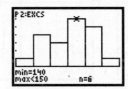 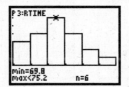

Appendix A **61**

Appendix B

Using the TI-83 Plus Graphing Calculator to Create a Histogram

1. **Resetting Calculator Memory** Turn on your graphing calculator and press [2nd] [**MEM**]. Select **Clr All Lists.** Press [ENTER].

2. **Creating and Entering Data into Lists** Name your lists before entering data. Press [STAT] and select **Edit.** Scroll up to the title bar (the "top shelf") and over to the first empty list beyond L6 (lists L1–L6 cannot be renamed). The highlighted "A" in the upper corner indicates that you are already in locked-alpha mode. Find and press the desired letters on the keypad. Press [ENTER] to title your new list for the resting heart rate data. Repeat for exercise heart rate and recovery time. Choose abbreviations that make sense to you—the names are limited to five letters. Enter all data.

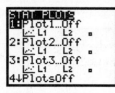 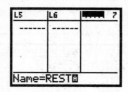 

3. **Setting up Graphs** Set up your calculator for graphing your data. Press [2nd] [**STAT PLOT**]. Select **Plot 1** by pressing [ENTER]. Use the arrow keys and [ENTER] to turn the plot on and select the third graph icon, a histogram. For the Xlist, press [2nd] [LIST] and scroll down to find your resting heart rate list. Press [ENTER] twice. Leave Freq. at 1.

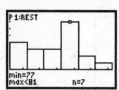 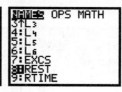  

4. Repeat **Step 3** to set up Plot 2 and then Plot 3, but do not turn Plot 2 and Plot 3 ON yet. The Xlists will be your exercise heart rate and recovery time lists.

5. **Plotting Data** Press [ZOOM]. Then select **ZoomStat** to see the first histogram, for resting heart rate. Use the [TRACE] and arrow keys to find the heart rate range that occurred in the class most often and the number of students that were in this range.

6. Press [2nd] [STAT] [**PLOT**] to turn off Plot 1, and turn on Plot 2. Press [ZOOM]. Then select **ZoomStat** again to see the class histogram for exercise heart rate. Then turn off Plot 2 and turn on Plot 3 to see the class histogram for recovery time.

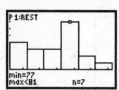 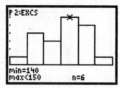 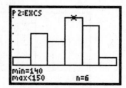

Copyright © Glencoe/McGraw-Hill, a division of the McGraw-Hill Companies, Inc.

Appendix C

Using the TI-73 Graphing Calculator to Create a Box Plot and Display Statistics

Note: If you have already used the calculator to make histograms, skip to step #4.

1. **Resetting Calculator Memory** Turn on your graphing calculator and press [2nd] [MEM]. Select **Clr All Lists.** Press [ENTER].

2. Press [LIST] to access an empty data table. Name your lists before entering data. Scroll up to the title bar (the "top shelf") and over to the first empty list beyond L6 (lists L1–L6 cannot be renamed). Press [2nd] [TEXT]. Use the arrow keys to select the desired letters, pressing [ENTER] after each. List names are limited to five letters. Go to **DONE** when you are finished entering the name. Press [ENTER] twice to title your new list for the resting heart rate data.

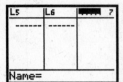 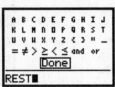 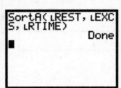

3. Repeat for the other two variables, choosing abbreviations for exercise heart rate and recovery time with 5 or fewer letters. Enter your class data in all three lists.

4. Order the data in your lists. Press [2nd] [STAT]. Use the right arrow key to select **OPS.** Select the default, **Sort A,** by pressing [ENTER]. The blinking cursor is a signal to insert your list names. Press [2nd] [LIST] and scroll down to select your first list. Then enter a comma. Repeat to select the second and third data lists. The commas will keep the lists separated so you can later investigate any relationship between variables. Press [ENTER]. With data sorted (in ascending order), you can easily determine the minimum, maximum, mode, and median.

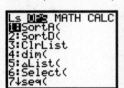 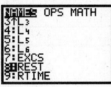 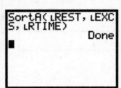 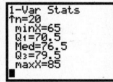

5. For statistical analysis, access the one-variable statistics for each list. Press [2nd] [STAT]. Use the right arrow key to select **CALC.** Select the default, **1–Var Stats.** Press [ENTER]. Press [2nd] [LIST] to retrieve one of your lists. Press [ENTER]. The mean (x) is the first entry. Scroll down to find the minimum (minX), median (Med), and maximum (maxX).

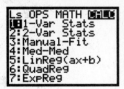 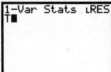 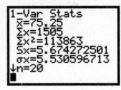 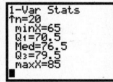

6. Set up your calculator for graphing your data. Press [2nd] [**PLOT**]. Select the default, **Plot 1**, by pressing [ENTER]. Use the arrow keys and [ENTER] to turn the plot on and select the seventh graph icon, a standard box plot. For the Xlist, press [2nd] [LIST] and scroll down to find your resting heart rate list. Press [ENTER] twice. Leave Freq. at 1.

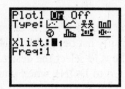
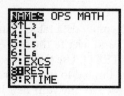
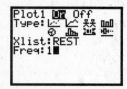

7. Repeat **Step 5** to set up and turn on Plot 2 and then Plot 3. The Xlists will be your exercise heart rate and recovery time lists. Because the data for all three lists is in the same range (about 60–160), all three box plots can be viewed on the calculator screen simultaneously. Remember that the first two plots are heart rates measured in beats per minute while the last plot, recovery time, is measured in seconds.

8. Press [ZOOM]. Select **ZoomStat** to see all three box plots, for resting heart rate. Using the [TRACE] and arrow keys find the median exercise heart rate. The left and right arrows will give you the minimum, maximum, median, and quartiles. The up and down arrows allow you to trace the three plots—Plot 1 is at the top of the screen. You also can see that the maximum the minimum heart rates and recovery times.

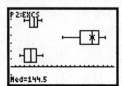
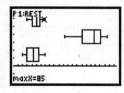
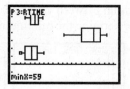

64 Appendix C

Appendix D

Using the TI-83 Plus Graphing Calculator to Box Plot and Display Statistics

Note: If you have already used the calculator to make histograms, skip to step #3.

1. **Resetting Calculator Memory** Turn on your graphing calculator and press $\boxed{\text{2nd}}$ [**MEM**]. Select **Clr All Lists.** Press $\boxed{\text{ENTER}}$.

2. Name your lists. Press $\boxed{\text{STAT}}$ and select **Edit.** Scroll up to the title bar (the "top shelf") and over to the first empty list beyond L6 (lists L1–L6 cannot be renamed). The highlighted "A" in the upper corner indicates that you are already in locked-alpha mode. Find and press the desired letters. Press $\boxed{\text{ENTER}}$ to title your new list for the resting heart rate data. Repeat for the other two variables, exercise heart rate and recovery time. Choose abbreviations that make sense to you— list names are limited to five letters. Then enter all data.

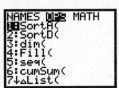 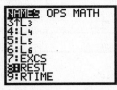 

3. Order the data in your lists. Press $\boxed{\text{2nd}}$ $\boxed{\text{LIST}}$ and use the right arrow key to select **OPS.** Select the default, **Sort A,** by pressing $\boxed{\text{ENTER}}$. The blinking cursor is a signal to insert your list names. Press $\boxed{\text{2nd}}$ $\boxed{\text{LIST}}$ and scroll down to select your first list. Then enter a comma. Repeat to select the second and third data lists. Then put a right parentheses ")" after the lists. The commas will keep the lists separated so you can later investigate any relationship between variables if you like. Press $\boxed{\text{ENTER}}$. With data sorted (in ascending order here) you can easily determine the minimum, maximum, mode, and median.

 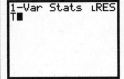 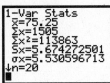 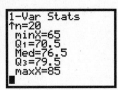

4. For statistical analysis, access the one-variable statistics for each list. Press $\boxed{\text{STAT}}$ and arrow right to **CALC.** Select the default, **1-Var Stats.** Press $\boxed{\text{ENTER}}$. Press $\boxed{\text{2nd}}$ $\boxed{\text{LIST}}$ and scroll down to retrieve one of your lists. Press $\boxed{\text{ENTER}}$ twice. The mean (x) is the first entry, then scroll down to find the minimum (minX), median (Med), and maximum (maxX).

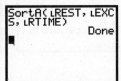

5. Set up your calculator for graphing your data. Press ⌈2nd⌉ [**STAT PLOT**]. Select the default, **Plot 1,** by pressing ⌈ENTER⌉. Use the arrow and ⌈ENTER⌉ keys to turn the plot on and select the fifth graph icon, a standard box plot. For the Xlist, press ⌈2nd⌉ ⌈LIST⌉ and scroll down to find your resting heart rate list. Press ⌈ENTER⌉ twice. Leave Freq at 1.

 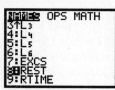 

6. Repeat **Step 5** to set up and turn on Plot 2 and Plot 3. The Xlists will be your exercise heart rate and recovery time lists. Because the data for all three lists is in the same range (about 60–160), all three box plots can be viewed on the calculator screen simultaneously. Remember that the first two plots are heart rates measured in beats per minute while the last plot, recovery time, is measured in seconds.

7. Press ⌈ZOOM⌉ and select **ZoomStat** to see all three box plots for resting heart rate. Using the ⌈TRACE⌉ and arrow keys, find the median exercise heart rate. The left and right arrows will give you the minimum, maximum, median, and quartiles. The up and down arrows allow you to trace the three plots—Plot 1 is at the top of the screen. You can find the maximum and minimum heart rates and recovery times.

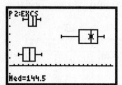 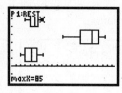 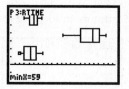

66   Appendix D

Appendix E

Using the TI-73 Graphing Calculator to Create a Circle Graph

1. **Resetting Calculator Memory** Turn on your graphing calculator and press [2nd] **[MEM]**. Select **ClrAllLists.** Press [ENTER].

2. Press [LIST] to access an empty data table. Name your lists before entering data. Scroll up to the title bar (the "top shelf") and over to the first empty list beyond L6 (lists L1–L6 cannot be renamed). Press [2nd] **[TEXT]**. Use the arrow keys to select the desired letters, pressing [ENTER] after each. Your title can only have 5 or fewer letters. Select **DONE** when you are finished. Press [ENTER] twice to title your new list for the plant type data at Site A. Make three more lists, naming them TOTA, PLNTB, and TOTB.

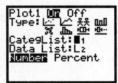
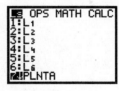

3. Enter your plant data. Because this data is "categorical" instead of numerical, you must use quotation marks around the first entry only. Place your cursor at the first entry for the list named PLNTA. Press [2nd] **[TEXT]** and scroll first to the quotes and press [ENTER]. Choose your letters, ending with quotes. Notice that a small "c" appears next to the title of a categorical list. Enter the rest of your plant types—you do not need quotes for the rest. Enter the total number of each plant in the next list. Enter data for Site B as well.

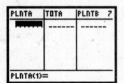
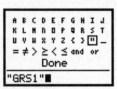
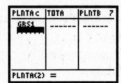
(fourth screen)

4. Set up your calculator for graphing your data. Press [2nd] **[PLOT]**. Select **Plot 1** by pressing [ENTER]. Use the arrow keys and [ENTER] to turn the plot on and select the fifth graph icon, a circle graph. For the CategList, press [2nd] **[STAT]** and scroll down to find your list named PLNTA. Press [ENTER] twice. Insert TOTA for Data List. Choose **PERCENT**. Always press [ENTER] to make your choices. Press [GRAPH].

5. Use [TRACE] and the arrow keys to view the labels and numbers for each sector. Notice that the calculator has calculated the percentage for you.

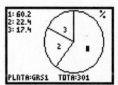

6. Repeat steps 4 and 5 to set up Plot 2 for Site B.

Appendix

Analyzing Probeware Lab Data Using Computers

The data collected during a *Probeware Lab* can be imported into a computer for further analysis. This allows the students to work with graphing software to perform more advanced functions than are available on a graphing calculator. Students can create different types of graphs and see the effect their treatment of the data has on the appearance of the graph. Students also can use the computer-generated graph to create reports, posters, and other visual presentations of their data.

Data lists and screen shots can be imported to a desktop computer from a graphing calculator with a **TI- GRAPH LINK*** cable. Each cable connects the port on the bottom edge of the graphing calculator to a free serial or USB port on a Windows computer or to the modem or USB port of a Macintosh computer.

There are several software options that are compatible with the TI-GRAPH LINK cable. Texas Instruments, Inc. has several programs that are written specifically for each type of TI graphing calculator. For instance, **TI-GRAPH LINK TI-73*** is used with a TI-73 graphing calculator. This software allows students to import screen images and data from the calculator to use in other word processing, desktop publishing, or page-layout applications. **TI Connect*** software is a newer software package with enhanced capabilities that also can be used to import and export information from the graphing calculator to a deskop or lap-top computer.

Texas Instruments, Inc. has another software program, **TI InterActive!***, that enables students to import Internet data, perform math calculations, and import data and screen shots from the graphing calculator. The program has a built-in word processing function intergreted into a single program.

Vernier Software & Technology has a program called **Graphical Analysis*** that has similar capabilities. This program was written specifically for science classes. It is easier to use than many business-oriented graphing programs and its capabilities have been tailored to fit the requirements for analyzing scientific data.

Importing data lists from the graphing calculator into **TI Interactive!** or **Graphical Analysis** enables the students to perform in depth mathematical analysis of the data. These programs have the capability of challenging students through the college level.

*   Refer to the appropriate hardware or software manuals for details about compatibility and capabilities.